So Many Unspoken Words

Kath Richardson

BLACK TREE

PUBLISHING

The author has made every effort to ensure the accuracy of the information within this book was correct at the time of publication. She does not assume and hereby disclaims any liability to any party for any loss, damage, or disruption caused by errors or omissions, whether such errors or omissions result from accident, negligence, or any other cause. However, if anyone can prove that errors have been made then please contact the author and she will be happy to amend the details accordingly.

For further information about 'So Many Unspoken Words' visit our website at: www.thewomanwhodidntexist.com

A CIP catalogue record for this book is
available from the British Library

ISBN 978-0-9955081-8-7

Design and Production by Black Tree Publishing
Gemini House, Lee Smith Street, Hull
Telephone: 01482 328677
email: books@blacktreepublishing.co.uk

Printed by: Fisk Printers, Hull

This book is dedicated to

Kazimierz Szwabowicz (1916 - 1973)
&
Maria Szwabowicz (nee Poleszczuk) (1927 - 1986)

PROLOGUE

It could be said that Kazimierz Szwabowicz and Maria Poleszczuk were unfortunate enough to be born in the wrong place and during the wrong era. Both had affluent and influential Polish parents and were blessed with a great intelligence which could, under different circumstances, have led them into successful futures. Yet they were born in the early twentieth century, which was a pivotal and painful time in their country's history, the consequences of which affected their lives profoundly.

Poland had always had a turbulent past, due in part to its unenviable geographical location, being lodged between two superpowers; Germany to the west and Russia to the east. During the course of its history, the nation had been moved physically across Europe several times.

In 1918, at the end of World War One, under the terms of the Versailles Peace Treaty, Poland had finally achieved independence, after one hundred and twenty-five years of Russian rule. However, over the next twenty years, their sovereign status was constantly under threat, with regular invasions of their borders by saboteurs.

During this period, Germany, never happy with the provisions of the peace treaty, had begun to find a new visionary in Adolf Hitler. Eager to re-establish Germany's power in Europe, he set out to create more living space for his people by taking control of the surrounding countries. By the late 1930s, he had moved his armed forces near the Polish border with the intention of claiming eastern Poland for himself. Ten days before the planned invasion began, he made it chillingly clear what he expected, ordering his commanders to kill, 'without pity or mercy, all men, women and children of Polish descent or language.'

Meanwhile, an equally dominant character had come to power in Russia. In the late 1920s, Josef Stalin had become the unopposed dictator of the Soviet Union and had instigated a reign of terror. He'd purged his party of all 'enemies of the state', by executing thousands of his own people and sending millions into the gulag system of corrective labour camps.

As Stalin began to witness the rise of Hitler and fear his anti-communism, he requested an alliance with Poland (as well as Britain, France and Romania). He was met with a refusal by the Poles who had no desire for Russian troops to enter their land. Instead, Poland made their own treaty with the United Kingdom and France, in the hope that if they were invaded by a foreign power, the British and French forces would come to their aid.

The Soviet Union, after abandoning talks with Poland, now decided to negotiate with Germany. In August 1939, the two great powers signed a ten year treaty of non- aggression known as 'The Molotov–Ribbentrop Pact'. More significantly, they also made an agreement to divide Poland between them- selves.

To this end, on the first of September 1939, the Germans attacked Poland from the west, causing Europe to be plunged into a Second World War .On the seventeenth of that same month, the Soviets attacked Poland from the east. In a matter of days, Poland was overrun, losing its independence and virtually disappearing from the map of Europe. It marked the start of a reign of terror in which most of the population were reduced to slaves and ultimately millions of them were slaughtered. It was the beginning of a nightmare that was to last for half a century, although the Poles bravely refused to surrender or accept this occupation of their country by their two neighbours.

On the 19th of October1939, the western district of Poland was incorporated into the German Reich and was ruled from Krakow by the Nazis' top legal expert, Hans Michael Frank, who became Governor General. The Nazis ruled by terror and civilians were shot and hanged for no reason. Thousands of innocent men, women and children were taken to concentration camps.

By the end of November, the eastern side of Poland was occupied by the Soviets and became incorporated into the Soviet Union. A mass deportation of Polish citizens began. They were transported to labour camps (gulags) in Arctic Russia, Siberia and Kazakhstan where thousands of them were to die from disease, starvation and exhaustion.

Residing in the eastern region of Poland (known to the locals as Kresy - although officially after the invasion in 1939, it became known as Western Byelorussia) were the Szwabowicz family. They included three brothers – the middle one being twenty-three year old Kazimierz who preferred to be known as Kazik. He had so far escaped Stalin's purge but always knew there was a distinct possibility that, as an 'enemy of the state', he would probably be arrested by the much feared NKVD – the Soviet State Police- followed by detention in a Russian labour camp.

Living hundreds of kilometres westwards, in the Polish capital Warsaw, were the Poleszczuk family - Dr Francis and his wife Maria. They were fully aware of the ever present threat from the Nazis, although they didn't belong to the most targeted group – the Jews. However, their twelve year old daughter – also known as Maria – had no idea that her childhood was about to end in the most horrific of circumstances.

What followed next in the lives of Kazik Szwabowicz and the young Maria Poleszczuk was a remarkable, life-changing journey, during which they suffered the most terrible injustice whilst witnessing human depravity at its worst. Their fortitude and the resilience of youth enabled them to survive but not without great cost.

Neither knew of the other's existence in 1939 but their lives were to become inextricably entwined in the future when they were exiled in England.

Their story is also significant in that it has been kept silent for the past sixty years. Little has been recorded regarding the exiled Polish communities who lived in Britain after the war and how deeply they were affected by their awful past. Even today many people in Britain remain ignorant of the terrible atrocities these people underwent, despite their vital supporting role, in World War Two, which helped secure victory for the Allies.

Although the world in general is aware of the huge numbers of victims involved in the Holocaust, they have limited knowledge of the immense suffering of thousands and thousands of innocent non- Jewish Polish citizens. This is partly because survivors, such as Kazik and Maria, were either ordered or strongly advised never to talk about the torment they underwent.

The Soviet Union particularly, were determined that the full extent and horrors of the Russian labour camps were to be kept hidden from the world. Consequently, archives have been closed, access to campsites has been forbidden and certainly, unlike the Nazi concentration camps, no television cameras were ever allowed to film the Soviet camps and their victims. Only in much more recent years have survivors come forward and spoken openly of their ordeals.

In several ways, the camp administration of the Soviets and Nazis were similar. In both cases, the victims involved were incarcerated mainly for who they were rather than for what they might have done. As the years passed however, the Nazis become crueller and crueller, sending millions to the death chamber whereas the Soviets did display a degree of humanity.

In 1941, the Soviets offered amnesty to most of their 'political' prisoners although unfortunately for many it came too late. On the other hand, the German prisoners of war had to wait until 1945 before they were liberated, many by American troops, as the Second World War came to an end. By this time, six million Poles had died yet only one tenth of these deaths were the result of military action. Of the twenty-seven million Poles who managed to survive, more than five million found themselves living beyond Polish borders, the majority for the rest of their lives. Kazik and Maria were just two of them.

Researching the twists and turns of their story has been immensely difficult. There have been endless unanswered questions and gaps in the exact circumstances of their incarceration. Frustratingly, most enquiries regarding Maria have drawn a complete blank. No records appear to exist of her captivity and perhaps, most pertinently, she was never willing to speak to anyone of her ordeal. Certainly her family never felt able to broach the subject, fearing to upset her.

After extensive research, mainly using archival evidence of their fellow sufferers, I have sought to be accurate with every detail regarding the Soviet labour and Nazi concentration camps. Some of the related conversations, powerful feelings and atrocities described in this story have had to be mere conjecture for no-one knows the exact horrors they saw with their own eyes and the resulting trauma these images created. However, one thing we can be completely definite about is the terrible legacy that resulted from Hitler's and Stalin's reign of terror- the effects were immense, far reaching and truly devastating.

As a couple, whilst enduring their suffering in silence, they always carried deep mental scars, as well as more obvious physical ones, and the cost of this was incalculable. Indeed the appalling after effects of their torment, have silently permeated into the lives of the next generation and beyond - with equally devastating consequences. As a result, this narrative will be harrowing to read at times but this was the awful reality of their experiences.

Sandra, Kazik and Maria's daughter, has been immensely brave in giving her permission for this story to be written, allowing the reader to learn things about her family which many would prefer to keep secret. She has done so, with one aim in mind. For years she has held a sadness in her heart and wondered why her parents never spoke of their suffering, never cried over their past but instead held it close, giving it a chance to ultimately destroy them. Now Sandra can begin to understand what was behind their silence and why they behaved as they did. Finally, she feels it is time to reveal their intensely poignant and personal journey....

CHAPTER 1
APRIL 1941 - EASTERN POLAND

Janek had only ventured into the forest to collect firewood when suddenly he became aware that he was in great danger. His heart began beating so hard within his chest that for a brief moment he was petrified, convinced the men would hear its thud and his whereabouts would be disclosed. Once he realised this was a senseless worry, he focused instead on remaining motionless.

For the last few minutes, he had watched intently as first one, then a second soldier had appeared within his sight; each poised with rifle in hand, searching this beautiful forest for people to arrest. Janek recognised them, with their blue- banded service caps, their khaki uniform and their knee-high black boots, as members of the much feared Russian Red Army.

He reassured himself that he was well hidden from view, as he'd positioned himself behind the trunk of a magnificent pine tree, which towered forty metres high, with a girth of almost two metres. He was also shrouded by a dense undergrowth of ferns and countless sedge which were covered by a dusting of snow. Despite this protection, Janek knew it was imperative he remain still and silent. His limbs were already numb from the bitter chill of the late wintery weather, so remaining immobile wasn't too difficult initially but for how long must he stay frozen to the spot? If he stepped to one side, any rotting vegetation under foot might rustle beneath his boots or some other innocuous movement could draw the soldiers' attention and then he felt certain he would be captured immediately.

He had always believed this forest to be impenetrable and relatively safe but now it seemed even the woodland was under threat and he wondered how much longer he could continue coming here. Even simple tasks such as collecting firewood or gathering mushrooms and berries in the spring, now seemed fraught with danger.

After what seemed an age, Janek could no longer sense the men's presence. Nervously, he tilted his head beyond the tree trunk and scanned his surroundings for any sign of further activity.

It seemed the militia had moved on, so breathing easy again, he felt able to adopt a more relaxed pose. Barely eighteen, he felt vulnerable and rather frightened, not that he would admit that to any-one but at the same time he was incredibly angry. How dare these Russian soldiers infiltrate his beloved homeland.

In fact, the Soviet army had invaded this eastern area of Poland some nineteen months previously, with the sole intention of incorporating the whole of the Kresy region into the Soviet Union and insisting that all inhabitants become Soviet citizens. To this end, they'd confiscated land, with no recompense for the land owner. Anyone who had dared to challenge their authority had been swiftly dealt with by the secret police – the much feared NKVD. They were renowned for their repressive methods and Janek had heard much talk of random arrests, imprisonment, severe beatings and even murder.

In recent weeks, they'd started infiltrating the local villages, carefully recording details of all inhabitants, following up their visits with almost daily checking of family members, along with documentation of their possessions. Now, properties were being regularly confiscated and the Soviet Army seemed to think nothing of destroying churches and arresting the priests.

To the Poles, most of whom were devout Roman Catholics, this was sacrilege and they were further incensed when they were forbidden to wear their crosses. It was also apparent that these Soviet Party activists were intent on phasing out Polish education; for they had started closing libraries, burning books, forbidding use of the native language and had even suggested that owning a typewriter was a crime. Many Polish natives were now being told they no longer had their jobs and to Janek and his fellow country – men, it seemed that hell had arrived on earth.

Ironically, the Soviets were justifying these aggressive actions, stating in their communist propaganda leaflets that they were relieving the people of 'their Polish yolk' and aiding them in their fight against Nazi Germany. What complete nonsense, Janek thought, such an unacceptable excuse for their abhorrent behaviour. He was incensed by their despotic actions.

Janek was very proud of his Polish roots. His father Antoni Szwabowicz had been an influential statesman, an ambassador within the Polish government and in his role as a Member of Parliament, he'd travelled to Russia many times. Whilst there, he'd debated many relevant issues with the Soviet leaders, including the on-going border disputes. So how dare the Soviet Union now impose its will, without redress and subject the Polish people to such despicable crimes. Indeed, what right had they to take ownership of not only others' land but this forest in particular? Areas of this forest actually belonged to Janek's father.

Sadly, Antoni had died prematurely in 1925. At just forty-three, he'd suffered a dreadful accident. Details had been scant but it was thought that he'd been mending the outside well when some masonry had fallen on his head and killed him outright. It had been an immensely sad time for all the family, especially as it had happened on Christmas Eve- the religious festival of Wigilia - as it was known to the Poles. Janek, only one at the time, had no recall of his father. But he'd been shown a photograph and it had left a vivid, lasting impression. Antoni, it seemed, had been a dashing young man with striking good looks and a flamboyant sense of style. Yet, despite his air of authority and the look of a strict disciplinarian, Janek had been assured, by his elder siblings,that his father had displayed both a loving disposition and a generous nature.

Janek treasured that image and always held his father's memory in high regard. In his eyes, this area was STILL Antoni's forest. Indeed, his family had had enough wealth and power to own several acres and Janek was determined to defend his father's legacy.

Right now, he loathed the Russians, yet he knew he was too young to join any rebel Polish army. He was more determined than ever to join the anti -communist partisans, who were forming groups all over the Kresy region, eager to resist this enforced regime of terror. However, Janek recognised that open confrontation was not a good idea; he owed it to his family not to put them or himself, in any danger.

Although he was the youngest son, he still felt a certain responsibility within his family, especially to his aged grandmother, whom he always referred to as 'babunia'. He – and his two older brothers and five sisters - all owed her such a great deal. For, soon after his father Antoni's death, his mother, Wladystawa (nee Matusewicz), had also died – probably of meningitis although no-one was certain. Wladystawa's mother had immediately taken the eight orphaned children into her care and had done her best, despite money no longer being plentiful.

They'd had a relatively happy upbringing with their 'babunia', all the children bonding together, showing great fortitude. Their daily existence had been a struggle but they'd learnt to adapt, endeavouring to support each other and enjoy opportunities for fun and laughter. In fact this resilience was proving a valuable attribute in their present situation. For now their focus was on survival of a different kind and they were determined to work together and maintain their Polish ethnicity for as long as possible.

However, these last few months, they'd lived in constant fear, acutely aware that the Soviet authorities wanted to remove all potential enemies and it seemed no-one was exempt. The NKVD's henchmen were forcibly making daily arrests for trivial, even fictitious offences and Janek was fully mindful that he and his elder brothers were especially at risk. Young, single men were recognised as obvious targets as they were seen as 'enemies of the state' by the Soviets- the ones most likely to pose the greatest resistance to this new regime. Every day, the three brothers faced the possibility of being taken away for interrogation, with imprisonment to follow.

Janek knew he must return home immediately and warn his family of the close proximity of the soldiers to their village. Cautiously, he gathered up his firewood, steadily retracing his steps through the woods. He paused from time to time, checking for any sign or sound of the enemy's presence. He left with a heavy heart – this outstanding forest, which he had enjoyed all his young life, would never have the same splendour or offer the same protection ever again.

Finally, Janek arrived back at his home located in Zupran, a relatively large village, situated in the County of Wilno. Living there were several hundred inhabitants, most of whom dwelt in single storey wooden houses, each with an outside well and a small wooden hut, enclosing a dry toilet. On many of the roofs lay remnants of the storks' nests, perched precariously on a horizontal wooden platform. The Poles loved the storks who returned every year to breed in the summer months, using the local lake to feed on frogs and insects. Every summer too, the streets of Zupran were vibrant with children's voices, as they played outside in the heat of the day whilst the farmers worked in their fields and their mothers laboured with chores. But today was the opposite. The streets seemed deserted as a freezing chill hung in the air and an icy layer of hardened snow covered the ground.

Then, as Janek rounded the corner, he spotted a small crowd gathered around the public bar in the main street, which was a popular meeting place for the men. He recognised many of them and acknowledged them politely.

Suddenly, as he passed by, he became aware of some-one tapping him on the back. He stopped and looked over his shoulder.

'Don't go home Janek, it's not safe for you,' the neighbour warned.

Puzzled, Janek dismissed this advice at first, 'What do you mean, it's not safe?'

'I'm sorry to tell you, your brother Kazik and sisters Eugenia and Werka have been arrested …just this morning. The NKVD arrived and simply took them away.'

'What! What are you telling me?'

Alarmed now, Janek's raised voice could be heard right down the street.

'I think,' replied the man, trying to calm the boy down, 'your grandmother is safe . ... she wasn't there when they came.'

Another man butted in at that point, 'Someone has reported your brother Kazik for speaking out against the Russian regime.'

Janek's eyes flashed in anger and he grasped the man tightly by the arm.

'Who?' 'Who has denounced my brother?' he demanded.

'I'm not sure,' the man answered, trying to free himself from Janek's grip, 'no doubt he was only trying to save his own skin.'

'Traitor.He's a traitor!' Janek cried out in anguish, whilst resisting the temptation to throw his precious firewood to the ground.

'Whoever he is, he'll pay for this!'

Four hours earlier – Zupran- Inside the   Szwabowicz household

Janek's elder brother, Kazimierz or 'Kazik' as he was known to his family, had been sat for ages in the kitchen warming himself by the range. A pan of soured milk was at his feet. He'd left the fresh milk overnight by the fire so that it would curdle and was intending to add potatoes later, to make a meal for his babunia and the rest of his family. Finding himself alone in the house, apart from his two sisters who were cleaning their bedroom, he had become deep in thought and rather sombre in mood, as he reflected on his past life, whilst fearing what might face him in the future.

Aged twenty–five, he felt that he'd already known more trouble than many men twice his age. Born in 1916, in what was then the capital of Russia, Leningrad, he had enjoyed a happy, safe childhood as the second son of respectable, prosperous parents. Yet by the age of ten, he'd witnessed the untimely death of both his father and mother. This had caused him tremendous heartache but he'd tried to find consolation by immersing himself with his studies, particularly enjoying mathematics at which he'd excelled. He had been determined to emulate his father, Antoni. Certainly he'd been told several times that he'd inherited his father's good looks, with his straight blonde hair and his attractive blue eyes, plus he had developed the same tall, slim physique. He'd also endeavoured to achieve a good education; recognising that his father had been highly intelligent and an influential man in Polish affairs and he had hoped to pursue an equally worthwhile if not similar career.

With that intention, after leaving high school, Kazik had enrolled in a Cadet School, based at Altyrelli in Zambrowie, to undertake military training to become an army officer. He'd generally appreciated the discipline it instilled with its strict regime and it had given his life both purpose and structure. He'd also loved all the opportunities it had provided for sport, particularly gymnastics, in which he'd displayed real skill.

But in 1938, this dream had evaporated. He'd been released early from the cadet school ... how had his superiors put it ... yes he recalled their words ... it was due to his 'health status'. Kazik had found that particularly hard to deal with, especially as since then he'd had no profession. Where did it leave him in terms of the future?

He deplored the latest Soviet occupation of his country and he desperately wanted to retaliate and join the rebel Polish army. His older brother Wladek had enlisted and Janek, who was almost eight years his junior, was already talking about joining the Partisans. Would his brothers succeed where he had failed? But then, as Kazik reminded himself, they were different in personality; they didn't seem to be plagued by such dark thoughts as he was ....

Kazik rebuked himself, he must stop this melancholy – the morning was passing and he must do some work .His babunia would be returning soon and she wouldn't be too happy to discover he had done nothing but stare into the fire. He bent over to pick up the pan by his feet when suddenly he heard a heavy pounding upon the front door. Startled, he froze for a brief moment – knowing that none of his fellow villagers would knock in such an intimidating way. Yet, if it was who he suspected, they would force entry if necessary, so it seemed pointless not to answer. Reluctantly, he walked through the small porch, used as a food store and nervously opened the door. He immediately felt the weight of several men pushing past him. There were five men in total: two he recognised as NKVD officials, two were obviously armed militia plus a civilian who was unknown to him. He learnt later that this was a legal requirement; having a civilian to assist with arrests legitimised the NKVD's activities.. or so they thought.

Immediately, he was aware they were holding him at gunpoint and it filled him with a sense of dread.

'Where are the rest of your family?' demanded one of the soldiers.

Kazik felt some relief that he could tell them that both his grand- mother and younger brother Janek were out of the house. But right at that moment, his two younger sisters appeared from their bedroom. Twenty-three year old Eugenia and Werca, who was almost eighteen, had been alerted by all the commotion.

'Lay face down! Put your hands behind your head and don't move,' ordered one of the NKYD officials, as he manhandled the girls. Utterly terrified, they did exactly what they were told.

The two officials then proceeded to search the house whilst one of the armed militia documented the exploration. Determined to be extremely thorough, they showed no concern over the upheaval they were creating. Drawers were carelessly emptied, mattresses were overturned and all paperwork was examined. On completion, it was apparent that nothing incriminating, particularly any fire arms, had been found.

Annoyed, one of the soldiers immediately seized Kazik, announcing,

'We are taking you away …….. you might be back home in two days…. after the investigation into your crimes.'

Crimes? Kazik was enraged, as far as he was concerned he was totally innocent of any misdemeanours but he was wise enough not to retaliate. What charge could they make against him? Hopefully, if he complied to their demands, he would be released without prosecution and allowed to return home.

Then one of the NKVD officials spoke up, his voice menacing, 'We have been told by one of your own people, that you have shown resistance to our regime.'

Kazik was stunned to think who 'one of his own people' might be and when he'd supposedly committed this 'crime' ….. although he did recall a recent evening he'd spent socialising with his neighbours at the local bar. He didn't usually partake of the vodka, so perhaps that was responsible for his loose tongue on that occasion. Normally, he wasn't confrontational but then these present troubles were not a 'normal' situation. He had such an absolute hatred of the Russians that he'd said so, in no uncertain terms … Maybe now , he realised, that hadn't been such a good idea but still he couldn't believe any of his fellow villagers would inform on him … although they might have been forced to implicate and accuse him, in order to reduce their own suffering. Who knows how he would react or what he might reveal after a severe beating or torture – he desperately hoped he wouldn't ever have to find out.

'Gather together enough food for two days and a few items of warm clothing,' the soldiers ordered.

Then they turned to his two prostrate sisters, still cowering on the floor, barking further instructions.

'Stand up. Go and do the same, we're taking you too.'

Kazik recoiled in horror. Why take his sisters? What harm had they ever done to anyone?

He wanted to protest vehemently but knew there was absolutely nothing to be gained. So, after quickly filling a small bag with provisions and some spare clothes, the three of them found themselves being frogmarched out of the house towards a parked vehicle, known locally as a 'Black Raven'. Just for a very brief moment, Kazik considered making a dash for it. He was sure he could outrun them and he knew an ideal hiding place deep within his father's forest but… no, it was obviously far too risky, he would be shot down instantly, besides he might jeopardise the fate of his sisters.

A crowd of locals had gathered outside and he could see the look of horror on their faces, as the three siblings were led away. The onlookers were totally powerless to help; besides many of them knew they would, undoubtedly, be getting their own knock on the door, before too long.

Kazik appreciated their silent support and it made him more determined than ever to stay strong but then neither he, nor his sisters, had any idea of the horrors that were awaiting them…..

CHAPTER 2
SIX YEARS LATER
AUTUMN 1947 - NANTWICH, ENGLAND

Kazik was really finding it difficult to adapt to English ways, especially the awful fish paste sandwiches and the milky tea and he certainly wasn't impressed with the British weather, particularly the mist and the constant drizzle. He was beginning to question whether he'd made the right decision to venture out on yet another wet, miserable evening. The heavy rain was certainly not helping to improve his appearance but, on reflection, did it actually matter? He felt sure the evening was going to be more of a night for the lads than an opportunity to meet some females whom he might want to impress. Not that he truly minded; he was just pleased to be getting out for once.

He really had been isolated since coming to England earlier in the year, feeling a complete stranger in a land that felt so foreign to him. Certainly, since his arrival, he'd not been having much success with the ladies. Why was it, he wondered?

He liked to imagine that although now thirty-one, he was still quite a handsome young man, with his swept-back blonde hair and his steel blue eyes. He was also relatively tall, with what he considered a good physique. His recent years in the army had built up his fitness levels and despite what he had undergone in the past, he was now happy with his weight. He guessed it didn't help the situation that at present he was working such long hours in a chemical factory in Northwich, which was understandably male dominated. Plus there were his limited language skills; whilst he could speak fluent Polish that was wasted on the local girls whereas his knowledge of English was almost non-existent.

He couldn't help but consider how different his life might have been if he hadn't been arrested six years previously and forced to leave Poland, his beloved homeland. Undoubtedly, he'd already be married to one of the local village girls and possibly even a father. Yet it seemed pointless to dwell on such things. What were his chances of ever returning home?

It had been a relief, back in May, to be commissioned into the Polish Resettlement Corps for they'd found him employment with ICI who, in turn, had offered him lodgings at Marbury Hall in Cheshire, a building which they'd only recently acquired. The Hall was set in beautiful grounds, surrounded by woods and fields which for Kazik was a welcome reminder of home, especially the wonderful trees and the magnificent lake that was used for fishing. However there was a certain irony, not lost on him, that during the Second World War, the Hall had been used as a prisoner of war camp.

The individual huts, on the former site, had been converted into two -bedroomed temporary dwellings for the many single men who were living there. Many of the employees were fellow Poles and gradually Kazik had felt relaxed enough to take up this offer to socialise with one of them after work. He'd especially thought it worth making the effort as it was an invitation to a bridge party. Kazik had always enjoyed playing bridge, not just for its mental challenges but so often, in the past, it had provided a wonderful release from times of intense boredom and frustration.

The friend had arranged to meet him at a certain house in Nantwich but because the town was so unfamiliar to him, he was having real difficulty locating it. The constant downpour was an added hindrance. Eventually he arrived, pausing for a moment, before knocking quietly on the door, really hoping it was the right house. A smart, middle- aged woman answered and after a rather difficult interchange in broken English, she invited him inside. Not wishing to offend, he wiped his wet shoes on the mat, took off his damp coat and patted his face dry, before he went in.

As he stood in the large drawing room, he became further concerned as there was no sign of his friend, indeed most of the guests appeared to be chatting away in English. Naturally reserved, he held back; besides, he wasn't entirely sure how they would react to him.

He'd already learnt that not everyone in England welcomed Polish exiles like himself, many believing them to be second class citizens. After the war, employment had been difficult enough for the English soldiers returning home, without the arrival of hundreds of able bodied Polish men seeking work. Also, he was aware that many English members of the left -wing trade unions were openly pro- Soviet, so they regarded the Poles with deep suspicion for what they considered to be their Fascist views.

Kazik had not encountered such hostility personally but then he hadn't mixed with many locals. Back at the factory, the workers were mainly fellow immigrants and at the Hall nearly everyone was a foreigner.

As he stood quietly, trying hard not to be noticed- rather difficult when he was over six feet tall- he felt himself being taken by the arm.

'Come, let me introduce you to two of my house guests,' the lady-host volunteered. 'They have recently come to England and are lodging with me at present. They have come from Poland, like yourself.'

Kazik hadn't understood too much of what she'd said but he smiled politely and willingly accompanied her, as she gestured him to follow on. He was pleased to find himself being introduced to two youngish girls.

'Polakow?' he asked them politely.

'Tak, Polakow,' they replied, shaking his hand warmly.

Kazik immediately felt less apprehensive as they invited him to join them.

Minutes later, his friend arrived and the four of them decided to make up a table. Kazik sat himself opposite one of the girls, who introduced herself as Maria, which meant they became partners, challenging the other two for a game. In bridge terms they chose to be 'north and south' leaving the other pair to be 'east and west.'

Kazik studied Maria quietly as she scanned her hand of cards. He couldn't help but notice how very attractive she was; such lovely dark, wavy hair swept back under a pretty bow, intense eyes of deepest blue plus her close fitting dress revealed a petite, trim figure. Although she had a somewhat sad demeanour, she appeared calm and smiled back when he caught her eye.

He was equally impressed with her skills at bridge – all the strategies she knew which helped them to win their first round– making the right bids at just the right time, knowing exactly when to double and redouble. What he wouldn't do to make a bid for her, he mused! Yet she seemed so young – barely out of her teens, he imagined. Surely she wouldn't be interested in him but he would, he decided, make the effort to be friendly at least.

When the first game ended and 'east and west' moved on to the next table, he took the opportunity to try and converse.

'Well Maria what brought you to England?' he asked.

Maria hesitated. 'I've only come here recently,' she explained, 'on my arrival I stayed in London for a while, then I decided to try life up north.'

'So, what are you doing for work?' he ventured, keen to ascertain more.

'At the moment, I'm employed at a local convalescent home ….as a waitress,' she replied rather coyly, feeling somewhat embarrassed that she had taken such a low paid, unskilled job, simply to survive.

'Whereabouts in Poland do you come from?' Kazik continued, disregarding her self- consciousness.

Maria faltered for a moment, 'I'm originally from Warsaw …. how about you? ' she asked, eager to avoid any further conversation regarding her former life.

'Although I was born in Leningrad … my family are Polish,' he explained, anxious to reassure her that he wasn't of Russian origin. Then, after a pause, he jested, 'We should have chosen to be 'east' and 'west' tonight, what with me coming from eastern Poland and you from much further west.'

'No,' Maria responded, 'We're Poles - so north and south suits us.'

They both began to laugh and with that, the next 'east and west' couple came to join them for round two.

Throughout the following games, Maria and Kazik enjoyed an intermittent conversation. Both of them tried to stay light hearted although occasionally there were moments of tension.

'I had to leave my hometown in Zupran when the Russians arrived in 1939 …but then you'll be too young to know anything about all the politics of that time,' Kazik remarked.

Maria felt slightly insulted, for he had no idea of either her great intelligence, her educational background ….or her personal experience of events in 1939.

'Maybe I am too young, at twenty, to remember all the details,' she replied, 'but that doesn't mean I'm unaware of events that happened in my country back then.'

Kazik became silent, dearly hoping he hadn't offended her.

For the rest of the evening, he couldn't concentrate. To be able to converse in his own language with such a beautiful but rather shy girl he found quite intoxicating. He couldn't deny he was smitten by this articulate, attractive girl but at twenty she was only a girl. It seemed very unlikely that she would be interested in a man eleven years her senior; undoubtedly this would be yet another girl he'd fail to impress.

His fears were unjustified. Maria was actually thinking how good it was to be able to speak with a man in Polish and a good-looking one too. Having only recently arrived in the country, she was feeling the constraints of her lack of spoken English. Ever since her childhood, she had enjoyed languages and had learnt in recent years to speak fluent Russian, German and Italian. Now her limited vocabulary was proving a real hindrance to making new friends and she felt rather lonely and isolated at work. Could Kazik possibly become a new male friend? Her initial view was that he was charming and sensitive and she was already gaining the impression that he genuinely liked her.

She was pleased at the end of the evening when he suggested they meet up again and together they arranged a suitable time and venue.

'I'll look forward to that,' she heard herself saying, 'perhaps, next time you'll have the chance to tell me more about yourself and your family.'

Kazik stared hard into the distance, lost for a moment in his own thoughts. Finally, he responded but his words came slowly.

'I'm from a big family … with seven siblings. ……..we were all very close – especially me and my youngest brother Janek. Then one day the NKVD arrived …. I was taken away in a 'Black Raven' and then …'

His voice trailed off as he took a deep breath. He shook his head, his face darkening as he struggled to say any more.

Maria reached out and gently took hold of his arm.

'It's alright, Kazik' she said reassuringly, 'I think I know what it is that you don't want to speak aloud. Believe me, I understand completely. ….Let's leave it at that.'

CHAPTER 3
APRIL 22ND 1941 - FROM EASTERN POLAND INTO RUSSIA

Inside the 'Black Raven' were individual locked compartments, where Kazik and his sisters soon discovered it was neither possible to sit or stand. They were just big enough to squat which made for very uncomfortable travelling. Nor could they see outside or have any idea how long their journey would take or indeed where it would end.

Kazik's mind was troubled but his military training had taught him to focus on positive thinking and the importance of staying calm. He breathed deeply and tried to counterbalance his racing thoughts.

He was desperately worried for the family he was leaving behind, particularly his babunia, concerned for the detrimental effect their arrests might have on her health. Hadn't he always promised to take care of her? What would her reaction be, on returning home, to find three of her grandchildren missing? How would she cope? He tried to reassure himself that Janek would still be around to support her, plus he knew his other three sisters would help, once they learnt of her plight.

Whenever the question of his betrayer's identity surfaced, Kazik told himself not to waste energy on speculation. Being a young man, with officer training, he'd always known he was an obvious target for arrest, in fact he felt fortunate to have avoided it for so long. Instead of dwelling on his accuser, he focused on the possibility that he might be allowed home within two days. Or was that an empty promise the soldier had given him?

Suddenly, his deep thoughts were interrupted as he realised the truck had stopped abruptly and parked up.

'Get out!' the driver ordered, as he and his sisters were released from their compartments and forcibly dragged from the vehicle. At first they stumbled, their numb legs refusing to work but, anxious not to annoy their captors, they forced themselves to walk as best they could.

Once out in the open, Kazik glanced around and guessed that they had arrived at Stara Wilejka, in Wiezien, a town one hundred kilometres north- west of Minsk and approximately two hundred kilometres from home. He was aware that this was the home of the regional NKVD administration centre and he felt sure, this was the building he was now facing.

Once inside, the three of them were taken into a heavily guarded prison room, full of many other detainees, all looking equally terrified. Then, individually, they were accompanied down a long corridor and placed in a further room for interrogation and documentation.

Kazik felt nervous when his turn arrived. After having his personal details recorded, a guard stepped forward and squared up to him.

'Face front.' … 'Profile,'   he commanded coldly as he took Kazik's photograph.

'Next, fingerprints.'

'Now remove all your clothes.'

Kazik wanted to resist this instruction but knew he had no option but to comply.

As he stood completely naked, he felt very uncomfortable, especially as a complete body search followed.

'Open your mouth ..Wider,' the man demanded as he placed an unwashed finger inside Kazik's mouth and around both cheeks.

'Tip your head back.'

Kazik tried to remain still as his nostrils were examined and his eyelids pulled down but his resentment was intensifying.

'Spread your fingers and swing your arms.'

The warden then checked that nothing was hidden in either his hands or under his armpits.

Worse was to come...

'Bend down, touch the floor…. No,legs wider.'

'Stretch your buttocks with your hand.'

'Take hold of your penis. Pull back the foreskin.'

The humiliation and embarrassment was intense. Kazik tried to show no reaction, not wanting to give them the satisfaction of revealing his rising anger. To think his sisters would undoubtedly be subjected to a somewhat similar ordeal, with such lewd levels of intimacy, was almost more than he could bear.

Feeling totally violated, more instructions followed. 'Get dressed but remove any shoelaces, belts, garters,' - the list went on and on – even underwear elastic was mentioned, in fact any- thing that the wardens considered might assist an attempted suicide.

Kazik was horrified. How was he going to prevent his trousers from slipping down? How could he walk without shuffling if his shoes were no longer tied? In other circumstances it would be amusing but to become an object of ridicule was totally degrading.

After completing these demeaning rituals, he was frogmarched away and allocated to one of the ten cells. He felt even more distraught when he realised that he was separated from his sisters but he reassured himself that Werca and Eugenia would hopefully be placed together.

He was now classed as a '*Zek*' – a prisoner – and his shocking treatment continued.

He found himself inside a cell that he guessed was barely six by four metres wide and obviously not designed for the many occupants it contained. Kazik estimated there to be more than thirty bodies, although it was hard to tell as everyone jostled together, trying to make space for the latest inmate.

He was instantly repulsed by the stench that greeted him. He soon discovered the culprit, as he was purposely manhandled to stand against it - a large barrel, acting as a latrine, known as a *parasha*. No wonder no-one wanted to be next to this fetid mix of human waste. Kazik baulked as he looked down and realised the barrel was overflowing, due to the sheer volume of use and that he was standing in a pool of filth. He tried to step aside but there was literally no room to manoeuvre.

A dim electric light-bulb hung from the ceiling which enabled Kazik to survey his surroundings; once his eyes had grown accustomed to the semi-darkness. He noted that the cell had a concrete floor, with just a single tiny barred window at ceiling height plus a small 'Judas hole' in the door, covered with a leather cloth. He stared hard at his fellow inmates, hoping he may just see someone he recognised. Many, he observed, appeared to have a bluish/grey tinge to their face, suggesting they'd been confined for more than just a day or two. He was also surprised to see many categories of people incarcerated – male and female, old and young, professional and peasant and some, he quickly learnt, were much more approachable than others.

'Watch out for the fleas,' one old man whispered, 'they like to attach themselves to newcomers.'

Kazik nodded politely but felt it best to hold his counsel, fearing to trust anyone.

After what seemed an age, some food arrived, via the Judas hole, although at first glance he felt it unfit for human consumption. Instinct told him he must try some, as it may be the only 'meal' of the day. He was repulsed as he sampled the watery, salty soup, known as *balanda*, disgusted by the thought of what it might contain...

'Fish entrails and potato peelings,' the old man informed him.

Despite its suspect content, Kazik forced it down, along with a small crust of dry bread.

Afterwards, he was relieved to discover that smoking was permitted, although for most of the inmates, their supplies had run out. Perhaps, Kazik mused, his limited supply of cigarettes might just be a useful source of bartering but for the moment he said nothing and simply observed the way of things.

It was now becoming clear that boredom was going to be a problem. Kazik watched as two men tried to play chess using make -shift pieces of stale bread but they were soon cleared away at the sound of advancing footsteps. It was the warden informing them that it was night time and they had to settle down.

That evening, he had to 'sleep' sitting up, leaning against a fellow prisoner, although sleep as such seemed an impossibility in such cramped conditions. He drew his knees up to his chest and wrapped his arms around his legs, trying hard to hold firmly onto his bag, anxious to protect his belongings from interference by his cell mates. He laid his head down on his knees and closed his eyes but he remained awake. Fetid air filled the room and every breath seemed like inhaling poison. Annoyingly too, the electric light was never switched off and every prisoner had been forbidden to cover either their faces or their arms with the one blanket they'd been given. Despite its appalling smell, Kazik desperately wanted to cocoon the blanket around himself as slowly the chill of night pervaded his entire body but he was aware of a guard permanently watching through the peep hole, ensuring this rule was obeyed. He felt his legs beginning to tingle as they gradually became numb but he had no choice than simply endure it.

His mind wouldn't settle as he both relived the dreadful events of the day and feared what the next day might bring. Suddenly, just as he felt himself drifting off, guards burst into the cell, calling out the initial of a name. All those with that initial, had to respond with their full name until the right prisoner answered. Then the required individual was dragged away, apparently forced along a corridor, past a stair-well adorned with anti -suicide nets and pushed into a room, located directly above their cell.

Perturbed and rather annoyed at the disturbance, Kazik muttered but didn't dare to complain too loudly.

'He's been taken away for interrogation,' whispered the old man, 'the guards always come at night and we never know what letter will be called next.'

'Could it be my turn soon, as I'm only in here for two days?' Kazik suggested naively.

His words were greeted by derisory laughter. Those awake knew differently ... many had been incarcerated for weeks...

Kazik continued to lay awake, hearing disturbing noises from above. Alongside obscene cursing came cries of sheer terror. Was the victim being assaulted, or tortured even, he wondered?

'He'll be refusing to co-operate,' spoke the old man in hushed tones, 'if you don't admit your guilt, you'll be subjected to a beating or worse.'

Kazik listened as the man went on to describe various tortures that were employed in the hope of extracting a confession. These included repeated beating with a revolver handle or a truncheon until the victim lost consciousness or the dreaded 'stoika' which apparently involved the prisoner being forced, for many hours, to lean against a wall on tip toes, supported only by their finger -tips.

After a while, unwilling to hear any more, Kazik pretended to be asleep. Suddenly the cell door opened and he found himself staring at the man whom he'd heard from above. The guards threw him onto the floor, with no offer of medical attention. As he lay motionless, blood poured from his mouth. It was obvious he'd had some teeth knocked out. No-one moved or said anything. Kazik felt powerless to help, instead he lay shaking, terrified of what was to come.

Several nights later, the letter S was called, followed by Szwabowicz. Jolted from sleep, Kazik was forced up the stairs to the very room he had only seen in his imagination. The cold was intense and the surroundings stark; white walls with no adornments and a single table and chair.

'Stand and face me,' ordered a nameless NKVD official.

'Now identify yourself.'

'Kazimierz Szwabowicz.'

'Why do you think you've been brought here?'

'I don't know.'

'What crimes have you committed?'

'None, I'm innocent.'

'If you were innocent you wouldn't be here.'

'And who are your accomplices?'

'I don't have any.'

And so the same questions continued, over and over again, without variation and so were Kazik's answers ... at first.

The interrogator, growing impatient, began to change his calm demeanour and started to curse. Kazik's eyes followed him as he went to pick up a lash.

He decided a change of attitude was needed. Knowing that the interrogator's objective was to extract a confession (in order to legitimise his arrest) he felt he had no choice – ultimately, he knew the NKVD could not be beaten, so what was the point of being a hero? Rather than face the inevitable assault, which would undoubtedly sap his energy and gain him nothing, he decided to sign a written confession. But if he hoped this was the end of his incarceration, he was sadly mistaken.

As dawn broke, he was escorted to the local court, adjacent to the prison, where along with many others; he awaited the morning 'trial'. Trial, he discovered, was a very loose term as it quickly became obvious there would be no justice. Within five minutes, he was declared, 'Guilty of being a counter revolutionary,' and then sentenced, 'You will be imprisoned in a labour camp for your 'anti- Russian' activities.'

Without any defence or any chance to appeal, Kazik was escorted back to his cell to await his deportation. He was overcome with weariness but by now it was mid -morning and he knew sleep was forbidden during the day. A great sense of foreboding filled his mind. The hope of an early release had fast diminished. Was there any likelihood that this mistaken 'guilty' charge might be revoked? He doubted it. Would there be any opportunities to escape or any chance of rescue in the near future? It seemed most improbable. And worst of all, knowing what he did about the horrors of Soviet labour camps, just what hardships were to come? He felt certain, there would be many unimaginable ones, possibly including the worst act that any one human being can inflict on another.

He knew from recent experience that his captors never displayed an ounce of pity or compassion towards anyone and that they had absolute power and control over all their charges. He hated them for their atrocities but just the interrogation alone had exhausted him mentally so he had no strength left to defy or even question their judgements.

He looked around at his forlorn cell mates. He had gradually discovered that most of his fellow inmates were a highly intelligent group of people and although they included both German and Russian captives, they had begun to cultivate a certain mutual respect for each other. Yet as Kazik saw their sunken faces and hollow eyes he perceived that most had lost all semblance of hope and were incapable of showing any sympathy or understanding towards each other's needs.

Despite the cell being crammed to capacity, Kazik suddenly felt totally alone in his despair. He recognised that his only choice was to accept his fate, however unwillingly, yet how WAS he going to cope? And if he was finding it hard, how would his sisters fare? And worst of all, was it possible that he might never see Werca and Eugenia again? The uncertainty of not knowing was torment enough, without the additional thought that torture might soon become a physical reality for him and who knows – for his sisters too?

He thought too of his babunia- how would she react when he didn't return? He pictured her deep blue eyes misting over and her wonderful smile being replaced by utter anguish and despair. Tears were close but he knew that weeping was not an option – how could he cry, when everyone around him would witness his sorrow? Instead he buried his head in his hands, cupping his ears, hoping to shut out the dreadful sights and sounds all around him. But there was no way he could block out the turmoil of emotions that were raging inside his head. Just what was to become of him?

CHAPTER 4
NANTWICH - 1947

Maria constantly thought about the handsome Polish man she'd met at the bridge party. She realised she didn't even know his age or anything of his background but she felt there'd been a real connection between them. It didn't matter that he was reluctant to discuss his past, for she was equally unwilling to talk about her former life. In fact this reticence gave them a common bond. It would be good to see him again and hopefully it would confirm how much she'd liked him. The day they'd arranged to meet couldn't come quickly enough.

Kazik was equally delighted at the thought of seeing Maria again, yet he was full of misgivings. Had he misread her signs? Had she simply been friendly towards him out of mere politeness? Would she even show up? He had so many self- doubts.

He was constantly plagued by other darker thoughts. Ever since his arrival in England, he'd been mentally torturing himself, dwelling constantly on his homeland and trying to picture the family he'd left behind, six years previously. He was trying to accept that maybe his grand- mother was no longer alive but had his two sisters survived their ordeal? Dreadful images of what might have happened to them constantly filled his mind. How too had the rest of his siblings fared, during those long years of war? Had they avoided arrest and gone on to marry and have children of their own? Even Janek, his youngest brother might have found himself a wife ..... assuming of course, that he hadn't been killed fighting in the war.

Yet, would he ever have the chance to find out and be reunited with them? He doubted it, not with everything that had happened during and after the Second World War; especially with Poland's loss of its independence. A return to Poland now seemed fraught with danger and no longer feasible. There was the genuine possibility of being rearrested if he simply set foot in his own land. In fact he didn't even consider it likely that he could make written contact. The irony of the situation haunted him. How little the English seemed to know of the Poles' valuable contribution to the

Allies' victory. How badly the British government had betrayed the Poles, taking the side of Stalin and allowing him to define the Polish borders.

He hadn't spoken of his concerns regarding his family to anyone but now he was wondering if he could trust Maria, even though he barely knew her. Perhaps, he could tell her the bare minimum, especially as she'd indicated her understanding of the Polish situation.

When the day arrived for their second meeting, both were feeling very nervous. They were naturally shy and being unsure of each other's feelings they simply exchanged pleasantries for a while. Gradually, as they began to relax, Kazik felt able to be more forthcoming.

'You haven't told me anything about your family,' he ventured. 'When did you last see them?'

Maria hesitated. She was still not ready to share her story. In fact, she'd found it easier in recent weeks, to lock all thoughts of it away. Her past was too painful to dwell on, besides she'd been told not to talk of it…

'I don't have any family to keep in touch with,' was all she said, before adding, 'but I'm guessing that you do, have you been able to make contact?'

Kazik shook his head.

'No, I haven't,' he replied wistfully. 'Remember when you first asked me about my family, I was really hesitant. That's because I actually don't know what happened to them after 1941…. You know, when the Russians arrived in our village. I was arrested along with my two older sisters. We were taken to the same prison but I've never found out what became of them after that. Nor do I know if other members of my family survived,' he confided.

Maria listened intently and after much thought, she had a suggestion to make.

'Perhaps it's time you made some enquiries, now you are settled in Northwich. Have you ever thought of trying to send a letter to your old address, just to see if you get a response? … I'm sure your family will be equally desperate to know you are still alive and to learn what happened to you.'

Kazik sighed. 'I have thought about it many times but I'm wondering if there's anything to be gained?' He explained. 'I doubt if my younger brother Janek or indeed any of my siblings will still be living in my home village of Zupran. I'm sure the

Russian take -over of the Kresy region will have forced them to move away to the non-Russian western side of Poland.'

'Yes but it's worth a try at least, isn't it?' she pressed.

'Not really,' he continued, 'If they did just happen to still be residing in Zupran, I don't know whether I could or indeed should make contact with them. I've heard much talk recently by some of the Polish lads in the factory that they've failed in their attempt to be reunited with family. In fact a few of them told me, they've been 'warned off'.

'Warned off!' Maria repeated, shaking her head in disbelief.

'Yes, it's true,' Kazik confirmed, 'Unbelievably, they'd been told that making contact could be 'detrimental to their families' now they are living in the Byelorussian Soviet Socialist Republic.

'I can see the quandary that gives them,' Maria concluded, realising Kazik would not want to bring any more trouble on his loved ones either.

After much hesitation, they agreed that it might be best to leave it for now.

Silently, Maria was pondering on other less charitable thoughts. At least Kazik still had hope that his family might have survived. If only she had such expectation to cling to, she'd be truly delighted. She had tried once to contact the Red Cross in an effort to trace her family members but it had been unsuccessful. Perhaps, she'd concluded, it had been too soon after the war but she doubted whether she would ever try again, it was just too upsetting.

But at this stage in their friendship, she felt it best to hold her counsel rather than show any ill feeling. Instead, with the more serious conversation over, she thought to try and lift their mood.

'Would you like to come along with me to the local Polish club?' she suggested, 'it's good to meet other fellow countrymen …. and you don't have to worry about speaking English,' she added with a smile.

After a little persuasion, Kazik agreed. The 'club', he discovered, had a dance hall with a bar and was obviously a popular venue for many new immigrants. The two of them soon found themselves chatting to another young Polish couple of similar age - Helen and Julian Novak - who'd recently married. The four of them bonded so well they arranged to meet up again, when their days off from work coincided.

Kazik was pleased he'd made the effort and thanked Maria at the end of the evening for giving him a great time. He bent over to kiss her and was delighted when she responded.

'See you next week?' he asked, 'Same time, same place.'

'Yes please,' Maria replied, as she went back for a second, much longer kiss.

Within weeks, Kazik was certain he had met the girl for him, though he hardly dare believe that she was as keen as him to make their relationship permanent.

Despite his fears and regardless of their short courtship, within eleven months of meeting her, he decided to propose. Why waste time? He knew all too well that a life could easily be extinguished in a second and that every day was important. He was delighted when Maria accepted and felt that his bad times had hopefully come to an end.

Together they agreed that their wedding should be planned for late November in 1948. As Maria expressed no particular faith, Kazik suggested the ceremony be held at St Anne's Roman Catholic Church in Pillory Street, Nantwich.

Next, they needed to consider where they were going to live once they were a couple because at the moment they were living ten miles apart and in single accommodation. Maria was rather taken aback when he suggested an option she had never considered.

'Before I met you, I actually applied to emigrate to Canada,' Kazik remarked, 'but it never worked out. Now I'm quite keen on the idea of going to live in Scotland.'

Maria was reluctant to consider such a move at first, thinking of the new friends she would have to leave behind. However, she quickly realised just how keen he was to go.

'I've heard there's a strong Polish community up north,' he explained, 'but actually, I've a good Polish friend living up there already.'

'Tell me more,' Maria asked, 'How do you know him- or is your friend female?'

'No! No! He's a male friend called Seweryn Lukas who's originally from Torun in Poland. He was my captain when I was fighting in the artillery division of the Polish 2nd Corps, during the war. He's a similar age to me and we've tried to keep in touch since we came to England.'

'So what's he doing for work?'

'He's studying agriculture in Edinburgh and has recently married a Scottish girl that he met at a local dance. He's actually done really well for himself as she's from a wealthy background.'

'Just as you've done well with me!' Maria said laughing, 'although maybe not the wealthy part! Who is she?'

'Her name is Elizabeth Newland Mitchell. Her grandfather – Steven Mitchell – was a well-known tobacco mogul and his family own considerable property in the Peebles area.'

'He sounds a great friend,' Maria admitted but her main concern was regarding employment. Would there be any suitable jobs available in Scotland for her husband and possibly for her too?

'I'll contact Seweryn and find out,' Kazik suggested.

Meanwhile, Maria was happy to let the matter drop. Despite certain reservations, she trusted Kazik and focused instead on planning her wedding day which was fixed for Saturday, November the 27th. Knowing two witnesses were needed for the ceremony, she would, she decided, ask a couple of her female Polish friends to oblige but with limited finances, it seemed sensible to make the occasion a simple, quiet affair, with just a few guests and no extravagance such as a reception or honey moon. It would be strange, knowing no family members would be present, but neither of them expressed any disappointment.

For Maria, her wedding day was going to mark the beginning of a much needed fresh start, so she had no wish to be sad by dwelling on a lack of relatives to invite.

The arrangements gradually seemed to be falling into place but there was one issue that was beginning to trouble her. Had she chosen wisely in agreeing to be Kazik's wife? She was meeting up with him on an almost daily basis and she was starting to see a different side to him. A small doubt began to surface in her mind. Was he the right one for her? Or was her foreboding just typical pre -wedding nerves?

She acknowledged that she felt genuine love for this man but what truly concerned her were the times he seemed so troubled and unhappy, despite his declarations that he loved her in return. She hated it when he would sit in silence and almost ignore her. Maria was desperate for life to be fun once more, for although still relatively young, she'd already lost too much of her youth to waste any more time being sad. Could she cope with someone who was so morose on occasions?

Although she understood his sadness over his missing family – was there more to his melancholy than that, she pondered? Had his months of persecution traumatised him so much that it had left him clinically depressed? She knew he'd been arrested and taken into exile but he'd never spoken in detail of his incarceration …. Just what had happened to him, she wondered? Maybe it was so unspeakable and so haunting, he couldn't let it go …

CHAPTER 5
KAZIK'S IMPRISONMENT/ EXILE - JUNE 1941

After languishing in prison in Stara Vileyka for several weeks, Kazik was totally unaware that political events in Europe were coming to a head. Hitler had begun to plan an attack on his former ally, convinced that the Soviets were planning a counter attack on Germany. Wishing to pre-empt this, 'Operation Barbarossa' was formulated and the German High Command began amassing a huge army, the greatest ever to face the Soviet Union, with a total of over three million soldiers.

On the 22nd of June 1941, the German assault commenced, moving easily and at speed, encountering little opposition from the Red Army who had been taken by surprise. One group of Nazi soldiers marched through the town of Kobylnik on their way to Moscow and the next city in their path was Vileyka.

Aware of this approaching German army, the guards at Vileyka prison were eager to remove all the inmates eastwards, following instructions from above. So, in the middle of the night, almost two months to the day of his arrest, Kazik, along with all other prisoners, found himself being escorted out of the prison, ready for '*etap*' (transportation).

As the inmates all gathered outside, Kazik scanned their faces, hoping to spot his sisters but disappointedly, they were nowhere to be seen. The long column of prisoners were then commanded to march in silence, five abreast, with their arms behind their backs.

'Keep looking straight ahead at the man in front of you. If you stop on the way or step out of line, it will be assumed that you are trying to escape and you will be instantly shot,' the guards commanded.

Kazik immediately felt great sympathy for the elderly, especially those weakened by months of captivity, who he knew would find it difficult to keep up. He just hoped the march would be a relatively short distance to their unknown destination.

As the hours passed, with everyone still marching, ever more wearily, the sun began to rise, revealing the half- light of dawn, enabling Kazik to become more aware of his surroundings. Just being able to feel and smell the fresh air was a source of utter joy after days of being locked in the stale and stifling atmosphere of the prison. Conversely, seeing the magnificent forests for the first time in many weeks caused him immense sadness. His thoughts turned to Zupran and his family. His heart ached for his grandmother and his siblings. He constantly fretted over Eugenia and Werca, realising they, in turn, would be agonising over his possible fate. Yet he had no means of telling them of his survival. In fact every step was leading him further away from home, with the awful possibility of never returning.

Suddenly, as the prisoners stumbled silently onwards, a deafening noise came from overhead. Kazik looked skywards and saw what he believed to be German aircraft attacking them directly. The convoy leaders began to panic and in the melee that followed, several prisoners were shot. Fearing for their lives, a few guards took the opportunity to flee and it took a while for order to be restored.

The column eventually reformed and carried on but it was unnerving for every-one. Kazik was horrified when he realised the significance of this event. If indeed the Germans were now invading Russia, as seemed evident, the guards would undoubtedly be driven to even greater depravities, through fear and in their desire to exert complete control.

At last, Kazik and his fellow detainees found themselves at a railway siding, with what appeared, at first viewing, to be a normal rail car.

'I don't think this is an ordinary train,' he heard one of the men whisper.

Looking at the long line of red cattle trucks, he had to agree, especially as he noticed the final truck was fitted with a 'cat' –a row of metal spikes, pointing down towards the tracks.

'That will be there to deter any one who might consider escaping through the floor,' he explained to a youth who was puzzled by them.

Kazik was also struck by the unusual amount of people milling around, despite the earliness of the hour. Not just railway workers and other civilians but large groups of NKVD officials and Red Army soldiers. The officials were heavily armed, their rifle butts glinting as they reflected the rays of the weak morning sunshine. Many of the guards had savage dogs snarling at their heels. They bawled their instructions to the assembled prisoners.

'Kneel down. Place your hands on your heads.'

Immediately everyone complied, although it was a struggle for many to stay still throughout the long process of documentation. After endless counting and recounting, all the exhausted prisoners were finally ordered to climb on board the train. The freight trucks were high off the ground and Kazik had to heave himself into his allotted carriage. He then turned round, offering a hand to a more elderly prisoner who was struggling to step aboard without the help of a ladder.

Once in the carriage, he assessed the basic amenities and realised the compartment had been adapted to offer sleeping facilities, providing a limited number of wooden benches. But his generosity had caught him out. Only a fortunate few had the chance of a bunk and the strongest members of the group had already claimed them. There was no choice but to sit on the filthy floor, along with the other unfortunate passengers.

As bodies pushed together, everyone trying to find some personal space, the guards arrived, slamming the heavy doors shut, and then bolting them in. It was virtually total darkness, apart from a splinter of light coming from a heavily barred window near the roof. The detainees sat in silence, most stunned by the recent turn of events. There was also the ever present fear that an informer might be amongst them; most knew that it would be most unwise to complain.

After several hours of inactivity, everyone was suddenly aware of a commotion outside. It seemed a second batch of civilians had arrived and each door had to be unbolted. Outside stood hundreds of bemused men and women, all newly arrested and interrogated, ready to be deported for their 'crime' of being simply Polish.

Kazik observed how tense all the guards were, screaming out their orders and viciously pushing the unwilling prisoners into the already overcrowded trucks. Their high level of anxiety, he surmised, was down to their own fear of being shot, particularly if they allowed any one to escape. Their ferocious dogs were now a great help, instilling fear and compliance, so that no-one dared to make a run for it.

As their door opened, Kazik was horrified at the vast numbers of people being manhandled into the carriage. The trucks were only equipped for little more than twenty- five occupants but he guessed there must be at least fifty extra people being forced inside. Would it be possible for so many bodies to survive in such cramped conditions or might they all suffocate?

But this wasn't the only shock. To his disgust, he realised a few of the newcomers were young mothers, some cradling weeping children. Then, horror of horrors... he spotted a girl who was obviously heavily pregnant. Yet no-one was given special consideration or offered any support. All were simply treated as if they were animals; in fact he likened it to cattle being taken to slaughter.

At that moment, he despised the Russians and everything they stood for more than ever. Yet it gave him a new resolve, a decision to endure what was to come and not allow himself to be beaten into submission. He vowed to uphold his Polish roots and traditions forever, even if it meant he might have to face an early death. If he was fortunate enough to survive what was to come, he would make it his mission to fight for retribution and freedom for all Poles.

Finally, when the carriages could literally take no more, the train pulled out of the siding onto the main railway line and its journey began. Kazik guessed they were travelling south – eastwards, out of Poland and into the depths of Russia.

He soon realised this situation was possibly going to be far worse than anything he had experienced thus far. Every minute that passed, the heat inside the carriage become more intense, as the rising sun gradually scorched the metal roof. The lack of air and space added to the claustrophobia, causing some to panic and struggle for breath. It wasn't long either before an overpowering odour permeated the entire carriage. This was caused by the inadequate toilet facilities- a small hole in the floor, which was often misused. With no provision of toilet paper either and completely lacking in any chance of privacy, it was an endless source of embarrassment.

As a woman went to relieve herself, on realising how awkward she must feel, Kazik averted his eyes but he was aware of other men leering at her which made him feel most uncomfortable. One resourceful mother made use of her flowing skirt, affording her young daughter some concealment but after a while most passengers became too exhausted to care who was watching them.

The following morning, everyone was experiencing desperate hunger pangs and Kazik realised they hadn't eaten anything for over twenty-four hours. The guards eventually arrived with their usual offering of soup, plus a small portion of hard, darkly-coloured bread. Most devoured it immediately but a few were wiser, keeping some in reserve, fearing it might be a long while before they ate again.

In the early evening, they were offered salted fish but it brought its own problem.

'When are we to have some water?' mothers asked anxiously, as their young children complained of intense thirst.

Water, they soon discovered, was rationed to once a day and offered to those with a cup. There was a communal cup chained to the wall but it meant taking turns which relied on the generosity of others. Kazik recognised that sharing would be the key to their survival but unfortunately it was obvious that some passengers had no regard for this ideal.

'I'll organise the distribution of water,' a passenger offered, with little intention of being fair.

'I'll be in charge of allocating the bread,' another man insisted, whilst planning to take the most.

Everyone viewed these passengers suspiciously but felt powerless to intervene as it was clear they were not men to be argued with. Most were '*urkas*' - genuine criminals -who were foul mouthed and totally intimidating.

The guards themselves appeared to condone the urkas' actions. Kazik decided this was probably because they kept the passengers submissive, making the guards' task easier.

The torment of extreme thirst continued to cause immense distress but the guards showed complete indifference, even forbidding them to collect water. The next morning, on discovering it was raining, Kazik witnessed a resourceful man reaching his mug beyond the bars of the window, hoping to catch a few drops. He hadn't realised there was a guard perched on the roof.

'I'll shoot if you don't stop immediately!' came the order, so he quickly withdrew.

For Kazik and most of his fellow passengers, the inhumanity of these guards was incomprehensible but far worse was to come.

Later in the week, the train came to a halt in a deserted area and all the prisoners were ordered to disembark, allowing the guards to check each carriage in turn.

'They're looking for any signs of break out,' an urka whispered to his friend.

Whilst this was true, they had a far worse reason for stopping. Over the following hour, everyone was forced to watch as one by one the dead corpses were removed from each truck. Some had succumbed to a contagious disease. Others, especially the oldest and youngest, had died of severe dehydration. But even worse to see were those who had killed themselves, using whatever tool they had found to slash their wrists. When no tool was available, a few had resorted to using their own teeth. Their bodies were unceremoniously dumped in piles, just left like planks of wood, causing further distress amongst the passengers.

After that, came a checking and double checking to ensure the numbers tallied of those now deceased and those still alive. Some of the guards had hammers and took delight in clipping each person's head as they passed by to be counted.

Eventually, the train continued its journey eastwards but suddenly there was further stirring and unease amongst the passengers. The word got round that they had just crossed the Polish border and entered Russia. Many started to sing and like a ripple, the words of 'We will not forget our land' were heard along the entire train. It made Kazik feel intensely home sick. Everyone had the same questions on their mind. Would they ever see their homeland again? Would they ever see the members of their family again? He glanced around the carriage but felt some relief when he realised he wasn't alone in trying to stem the tears. In fact many were sobbing openly.

The train continued its journey deeper into Russia, kilometre after kilometre, hour after hour with no explanation. Eventually, at the end of their second week, it came to a final halt. It had arrived, in the dead of night, at the historic city of Ryazan, one hundred and twenty miles to the south east of Moscow. The carriage doors were opened for the last time and the weary prisoners were removed and ordered to walk to an open area. Once again, they were made to squat with their hands on their heads, a tactic used to avoid escape, whilst the tedious routine of counting took place. From there they were taken in *voronoks* (black vans) to their allocated prison. They had arrived at Labour camp number 178 where, unfortunately, their nightmare was to continue.

CHAPTER 6
NANTWICH - AUTUMN / WINTER 1948

Maria was trying to rationalise her fiancé's recent subdued, rather disturbing behaviour, reassuring herself that he was just a sensitive man who had been through so much. Her earlier life had also been extremely traumatic but she was adamant it wasn't going to spoil her future. She endeavoured to enjoy the time spent with Kazik and keeps his mood uplifted, hoping he would begin to accept his new life in England. It was good when they shared times of closeness as this reassured her that their love for each other was genuine, despite him never expressing the true depth of his feelings.

One area of their relationship where he was always vocal was his insistence that whenever they met, they must converse only in Polish.

'Don't you think we ought to practise our English together?' Maria suggested one evening, 'Now we are living here, I feel we should make the effort to learn the language.'

Kazik shook his head vehemently for he had no desire to 'become English', as he saw it.

To this end, he was happy to socialise at the Polish club on a regular basis and maintain their friendship with the Novaks. Together, they shared Polish meals and reminisced about their homeland.

Maria was far more willing to try and adopt the British way of life but any misgivings she felt about her decision to marry Kazik, she kept to herself. She was totally unaware that he was having doubts of his own. One evening, as they sat relaxing together, he made a startling announcement.

'Maria, I have something important to say and I know it won't please you.'

She stared at her fiancé anxiously, what was he going to suggest now? Had his plans to go to Scotland altered? Had he found employment in a new area of the country? She truly hoped not. She certainly wasn't expecting what came next.

'I'm sorry Maria but I can no longer marry you,' he blurted out, almost coldly, disregarding the hurt this might cause.

What! Had he changed his mind so near to the wedding? What had led to this decision she wondered? Surely he'd not met some-one else? Perhaps he'd decided she was too young after all?

'Why Kazik? Why?' was all she could repeat.

It seemed an age before he replied. Then the words came in a torrent, 'Because you and others have been sent from the Russian police to kill me!'

'What! What are you talking about Kazik?' Maria asked, totally thrown by such a strange comment.

He simply repeated his explanation and stared at her with that deep intensity that was becoming so familiar. In fact she was almost more concerned by the look in his eyes than the content of his words. She saw a terror in them which she found most perturbing. She was convinced he was suffering delusions and that this wasn't an actual rejection of her.

For the next few minutes, she frantically tried to reassure her future husband, telling him his fears were totally unjustified and that he was safe, now he was residing in England.

'No-one is trying to kill you Kazik. You aren't thinking straight,' she whispered.

He didn't respond initially but after a few minutes he began to calm down and he reached out to hold her. Maria didn't rebuff him but she felt deeply perturbed by this accusation. She began to consider if it was time to pull out of the relationship. But then … she had seen something in Kazik's pain which she could identify with and now it was apparent how much he needed her. She, more than anyone, was well qualified to understand what might lay behind his angry outbursts, so she felt able to forgive him. She tried to assure herself that hopefully this paranoia would disappear with the passing of time..

Over the following days, Kazik's moods continued to swing and Maria was never sure what triggers would set off his delusional thoughts. At times, he was genuinely loving and sensitive, saying he was more than happy to go ahead with the wedding but on other days he was distant and unresponsive.

Maria still reasoned that once married, and settled in Scotland, he would surely recover, especially with her support and encouragement.

'It looks like we could have a lovely warm day for the wedding,' Maria remarked, in early November, as all of Britain had recently enjoyed a mild spell.

Kazik nodded in approval, 'I'll keep you warm, what - ever the weather,' he laughed as he put his arm around his fiancée.

'Well that's the best forecast I could wish for!' Maria responded, feeling more at ease.

Disappointedly, when the big day finally arrived, the temperature had plummeted but both of them were determined not to let it spoil their day. Although a simple affair, they both really enjoyed the occasion. Maria was thrilled by how handsome Kazik looked in his army uniform whilst he was equally proud of his beautiful, young and very trim wife. They both hoped this was the start of some really good times ahead, although now they'd planned to move it was hard for Maria to leave her new found friends behind.

A few days later, they found themselves travelling up north by train to an unknown future. They'd located lodgings in Hamilton, near Glasgow, in a house where other Poles were residing. Fortunately, Kazik had managed to secure employment in a local factory, once again with the help of The Polish Resettlement Corps.

Over the coming days, Maria accepted her role as a stay at home wife and was happy, always ensuring she kept a clean house and cooked her husband his favourite Polish meals. She also enjoyed the intimacy of married life and responded to Kazik whenever he was in a loving mood.

However, as days passed, Maria began to feel her life was not going quite as smoothly as she had hoped. She was finding it especially difficult to make new friends; her language skills although improving, were now challenged by the Scottish dialect. All this use of the word 'wee' left her baffled and to be called a 'hen' she thought most odd.

However, it was good to laugh at such idiosyncrasies because she realised that life was becoming rather dull. She still had little doubt that her husband loved her dearly and was happy to be married. The issue that particularly troubled her was his increasingly unresponsive attitude to every-day life. It wasn't just the fact that he wouldn't communicate and explain what was bothering him; he had become so withdrawn, even rather sullen on occasions and appeared to not even notice her.

She accepted that her husband was a reserved man who rarely spoke out or demonstrated his inner feelings but the affection and attention she craved was not as forthcoming as she had hoped.

Recalling former incidences of irrational behaviour, she was still convinced this morose aspect of his personality was the result of trauma from his dark past. Maybe it would help them both if he could just share and speak out about his experiences, with her at least. Yet, she knew only too well how difficult that was - why would you want to talk of things so evil that they defied belief.

CHAPTER 7
RYAZAN CAMP, RUSSIA - SUMMER 1941

Kazik, along with all the other disorientated passengers, surveyed his new 'home'. His first sight was a large fence surrounding the perimeter of the camp which comprised of wooden posts, with rows of barbed wire horizontally positioned in between each one, then a further two rows stretched diagonally across. The camp itself was entered through a gatehouse which had an illuminated sign above it extolling the Soviet virtues with words to the effect of 'Work in the Soviet Union is glorious and honourable.'

The majority of prisoners were so bewildered and traumatised they barely noticed the sign, let alone pondered on its significance. As the gates closed firmly behind them, their thoughts were much more focused on their physical need for food and their overwhelming desire for somewhere to lay their exhausted bodies. However, neither of these needs was of any importance to their new captors. They would have to wait.

The immediate priority was to have their paper work checked by the camp commander who was waiting at the camp allocation office. This was a time- consuming job which was followed by another equally drawn out procedure – the *poverka or* roll call. For this, all the new arrivals were marched into a large open space (*the zona*) in the centre of the camp.

As the rows of prisoners lined up in silence, many barely able to stand, Kazik surveyed his surroundings and realised it was a fearful God- forsaken place to be. The camp itself appeared to be laid out in a square with row upon row of identical primitive wooden huts. In the centre was a high watch tower where he surmised guards would be observing prisoners to ensure no-one attempted escape. This was duly confirmed after *poverka,* when a stark warning was issued.

'If you enter that forbidden zone, beyond the boundary fence, you will be instantly shot,' explained a young guard without any hint of emotion.

Next every prisoner was called, within a small group, for 'cleansing' – the ritual shaving, showering and delousing. After undressing, they were ordered to throw their ragged clothes into a heap to be disinfected with chemicals and then heated in boiling water. For some, the lice fell off their naked bodies in handfuls. Next came the full body shave which was detested by every-one. Bathing followed, at the *banya,* but it was merely a quick shower with so little water and a sliver of black, evil smelling soap that it was impossible to get clean. Then, after a complete dousing with anti- lice powder, came the forced line up for the retrieval of their de-fumigated garments.

The next few minutes were extremely fraught as the urkas handed clothing out at random, after first taking the best ones for themselves. No-one was given their own clothes back and Kazik watched in disbelief as men fought each other for items that weren't worthy of argument, they were so threadbare.

'You son of a bitch, that's my jacket!' a man screamed as he grabbed it from a younger man. He was adamant because the jacket had his camp number on it.

Fighting broke out but the guards disregarded it, leaving it up to individuals to sort it out for themselves. A few began to swap items with their fellow prisoners, some resorted to bartering to try and gain better garments whereas Kazik quickly dressed with what he'd been given, preferring to be covered than stand naked and argue over them.

It wasn't long before he was called to the examination room, characterised by its clean white walls and bare wooden floor. A young female doctor began by inspecting his eyes, ears, teeth, tongue, nose and throat. She then asked him to breathe deeply and cough repeatedly. She listened to his heart and pressed on his intestines, kidneys and liver. Despite Kazik's stomach feeling sore, he tried hard not to wince. Next came a series of exercises, including running on the spot for five minutes and twenty- five sit-ups.

As Kazik caught his breath, he waited in fear, knowing what was still to come. He gritted his teeth and tried to put his mind elsewhere as she carried out the dreaded internal inspection. Fortunately, it was over quickly.

Suddenly he was aware of her talking to the NKVD officer who was present:

'First labour category. No restrictions.'

He watched carefully as the officer wrote on his file ' TFT'.

He soon figured out that this indicated he was relatively healthy and would therefore be given harsh physical labour as opposed to lighter duties.

'Haven't you realised, all of the Polish prisoners, regardless of their health or age, are allocated the hardest categories of work,' a fellow Pole informed him.

This obvious bigoted hatred was not unexpected but it was still hard to take.

'I guess there is absolutely nothing we can do about it either,' said another.

Their first shift was apparently due to begin early the next morning, with no allowance being made for the fact that they'd just arrived after an extremely long journey. Nor had they been offered any food. Eventually, all the detainees were ordered to line up outside the *stolovaya* – the camp dining hall.

Kazik joined a long queue that was remarkably orderly considering the extent of their hunger but the fear of reprisal, as they were under constant surveillance, was utmost in their mind. Finally, his turn came but the soup offered was foul-tasting.

'Pig slops,' was the description one man gave it.

'It's made of dog meat,' another suggested, 'or maybe made with one of the dead horses.'

'I'm told that animal lungs are used,' a long term prisoner explained.

'No wonder it tastes so repulsive,' another spoke out, with most nodding in agreement.

The accompanying bread was no more palatable. It felt wet and resembled clay but all agreed it was better than nothing.

The other problem that soon became apparent was the lack of cutlery and crockery. Kazik quickly realised that his spoon was such a valuable item he would need to keep it well hidden in order to avoid pilfering.

On completion of their 'meal', they were all asked to line up, ready to be placed in small groups, known as brigades and then allocated barracks.

Once inside, Kazik viewed his new surroundings with some foreboding. He reckoned the single room was no more than seven metres square yet it appeared upward of eighty people were to be crammed inside. He was grateful that most of the inmates appeared to be fellow Poles.

After a brief introduction to their brigade leader - the *starosta*- a high status prisoner who was responsible for keeping order- they were each allotted a wooden bunk. The bunks, made from the local larch trees, were laid out in rows, four tiers high. Kazik smiled to himself when he discovered they were referred to as 'cots'. I doubt if I'll sleep like a baby he thought to himself and he was right. No bedding was provided, apart from one very foul smelling blanket which was needed for cover, so he had to sleep directly on the hard wooden plank. He observed that his fellow prisoners all kept their clothes on and slept on their backs. The best bunks were at the top but he was given the one nearest the bottom, furthest from the stove. It resulted in limited sleep as he struggled with cold and discomfort.

It seemed like the middle of the night when an ear piercing siren woke everyone up, ready for a very early breakfast. It was a welcome bowl of porridge but there was little opportunity to savour it. Within five minutes a second siren sounded, followed by an order to line up in front of the camp gate for the morning count.

'My belly is still virtually empty,' moaned one of the men as he went to stand with the four others in his group.

Although he'd spoken under his breath, a guard immediately approached him.

'Be quiet!' he snapped as he struck him viciously with his rifle butt. The man clasped his head in pain but said no more.

After the count, the starosta spat out a range of instructions explaining they were at the camp to work and that everyone must contribute to the camp's production plan.

'It is essential that each member of the brigade fulfil a 'norm'. A norm is dependent on your allocated assignment. If it is not completed, we will all suffer as we will all lose some of our food rations,' he explained.

Then a further explicit and chilling warning followed: 'You work, you eat, you stop working, you die. For I will not allow any of you to jeopardise my chance of food, any ineptness on your part will not be tolerated.'

With heavy hearts, the prisoners set off towards a huge forest, accompanied by guards and their equally aggressive German shepherd dogs. Immediately orders were given, 'A step to the left or the right will be considered an attempt to escape. The convoy will fire without warning. March!'

'Guards who shoot escaping prisoners receive money,' one of the prisoners whispered to his comrades, 'so be sure to do as they say.'

As the column continued, this threat became all too real. One of the leaders suddenly shouted at a more elderly prisoner, 'Hey bring me that plank!'

The man faltered as he tried to protest, 'But it's across that fence…

'That doesn't matter, now go!'

Too frightened to refuse, the unfortunate victim slowly stepped out of line and was immediately gunned down. The other prisoners gasped at this cruelty. Many began to visibly struggle as the terrain became more difficult and one of the older members of the party fell down in exhaustion. Those around him held their breath. They watched nervously, as his brigade leader insisted, 'You walk or you die.'

'If you will just give me a short rest, I will catch up,' the man begged.

With that a shot was heard and the man fell silent. It wasn't long before a second prisoner had stumbled but this time he was a much younger man. Once again Kazik and his fellow prisoners watched uneasily, waiting for the inevitable. Yet this time a provisions' cart appeared and the youngster was thrown onto it. After allowing him a few minutes to recover, the youth was ordered to re-join his party. He was grateful to be saved but attributed it solely to the fact he still had the capacity to work.

It was a submissive group that finally arrived at a large clearing, ready to be allocated appropriate tasks. First, they had to be recounted, just to ensure that no-one had actually managed to go missing en-route. Did they really imagine anyone had escaped? The only ones missing are those you've shot, thought Kazik, as he lined up unwillingly. As the officials wandered among the prisoners, they began to bark out different orders, according to the age and outward appearance of the men.

'Stretch out your arms,' they said to some, feeling their muscles.

As a result, each man was allocated one of a variety of chores. 'You are to work as a lumberjack…. you down the coal mine … you as a carpenter,' the list went on. Kazik and his party were ordered to break rocks and dig ditches. He was grateful that he was relatively fit but this hard manual work soon sapped his limited strength. Nor could he understand why they were give the most inappropriate, poor quality tools and he particularly struggled with a very cumbersome wheel barrow. Yet the frantic demands of the guards meant he could never slacken his pace.

He was grateful to be out in the open but there were incessant flies buzzing around which bit into his skin, creating terrible itching and causing his eyes to swell. He slapped them repeatedly but he tried to push on, eager to complete his norm. He was surprised when the foremen allowed a smoke break but its benefits were quickly diminished. 'Right, the time you've taken for your break, will have to be made up at the end of the shift.'

After twelve, very long hours, the men were finally allowed back to camp. Many were struggling not just with total fatigue but at the thought that tomorrow would be no different.

'I'm even thinking those of our men who have been shot are better off than us,' one of the sicker prisoners remarked.

'Yes, even suicide seems almost preferable to this,' another agreed.

That evening, Kazik, along with the majority, were grateful that at least they'd earned their full quota – their four hundred grams of bread, ten grams of sugar plus a half litre of soup made with hot water and groats- all calculated to be the minimum amount required for survival. After the 'meal' came a further poverka, followed by the siren, heralding a very welcome time ….sleep.

The men in the barracks appeared to be friendly at first. In the evenings that followed, they played games of cards or chess and enjoyed an occasional smoke together. But slowly Kazik learnt it wasn't wise to be too familiar with others, particularly the *urkas*. For he observed, as in the train, there was a hierarchy within the inmates and it was the urkas (the professional criminals) who dominated camp life. They were certainly given all the best jobs whist wielding control over all the political prisoners. Just why were they so powerful?

Kazik began to study them closely. They seemed easily distinguishable with their own distinctive style of dress. Every morning, he watched as they folded down the tops of their leather boots, covered their heads with a peak-less leather cap and wore an iron cross around their neck. Kazik doubted this had any religious intent, especially as some were painted with pictures of naked women. Occasionally, he would catch a glimpse of bluish tattoos, emblazoned on their chests, stomach and back. These intrigued him, even causing him to smile. Some tattoos were sentimental: 'I'll never forget my mother', others artistic – eagles flying through the air whilst some erotic – showing couples engaged in sex. What women would want them, thought Kazik and surely their mothers would prefer to forget them. He was especially appalled by their use of the vilest and abusive language he'd ever heard. They even had their own slang vocabulary which they expected all the prisoners to learn.

'You must learn to speak *blatnoe slovo* –'thieves' talk,' they ordered, almost as an induction ritual. Kazik, along with most of his fellow political prisoners, learnt that the best tactic was to try and avoid them, although this wasn't easy. It was almost impossible not to feel the influence of their lewd behaviour, especially on occasions such as the monthly ablutions.

All the inmates were expected to attend 'delousing sessions' followed by bath times, to prevent the spread of disease. Far from being the more pleasant aspect of camp life, as they should have been, the prisoners came to dread them. It was hard enough that these sessions came at the end of an exhausting day's shift, but the urkas used them as an opportunity to vent their sexual frustration on unwilling participants. Kazik did his best to stand furthest away from them, hoping not to attract their attention but being naked always made him feel very vulnerable.

The ones who suffered most were the women. They were treated with complete indifference and in many cases great brutality. Kazik and his fellow prisoners were forced to stand by and watch as women were grabbed by the throat, thrown to the ground or pushed against a pile of logs to be sexually assaulted. Some yelled in terror, which the urkas simply ignored and sadly too, so did everyone else. Other women accepted it, seemingly used to it, so offered no resistance. Certainly all prisoners had become accustomed to seeing men and women, in full view, being intimate out in the open, some consensually but most not.

Kazik was shocked that sex was so public and rape so outwardly acceptable. Nor could he tolerate the fact that the perpetrators were only mildly rebuked by the guards. 'Come, come boys, have you no shame?' was the most they would utter as they walked past.

His mind turned to his two sisters. He couldn't bear to think they might be going through similar abuse. After witnessing yet further rapes of young women and even some teenage boys, the intensity of his repressed anger, especially towards the urkas, escalated. He stored these dreadful images in his mind and they haunted him yet he knew he must keep silent, aware that an outburst or any attempt at revenge would have punishable consequences. Instead he simply withdrew further into himself. His mind was in such turmoil, he began to imagine that everyone was against him. He felt absolutely nobody could be trusted, even fearing some of his fellow prisoners who had showed a measure of friendship, believing now that they had been simply feigning kindness.

As well as this mental trauma, the lack of food, its poor quality and how to gain more of it was becoming an exaggerated focus in his daily life. The Russian authorities were so preoccupied fighting the Germans; food deliveries to the gulag were not a priority and often failed to arrive. The limited food that was available went to the guards and urkas first, which reduced supplies even further. The totally unacceptable rations had begun to take a dreadful toll. All prisoners were displaying the early stages of malnutrition, with loose teeth and deep skin sores whilst many were ill with diseases such as scurvy, pellagra, and typhoid which created unbearable problems.

Although Kazik hadn't, as yet, succumbed to any of these more serious complaints, when he awoke every morning, he felt strangely dizzy and disorientated. It was always a huge effort to get up or even to walk over to the dining hall, despite the likelihood of a meagre amount of sustenance. He realised, like everyone, he had set out on the road to starvation. In fact in his darkest moments, he began to question the point of thinking about tomorrow or the next day when each day could well be his last.

He witnessed, within his own barrack, men becoming so hungry and sick, they were rendered incapable of any mobility or rational thought. He was adamant he didn't want to join them, reminding himself not to give up hope. He forced himself to focus on his one goal – to escape this suffering and be reunited with the family he loved so much. This was immensely difficult when nearly every waking minute was spent thinking about food or rather the unbearable lack of it.

On his return journey to camp every evening, it was torment to observe many in the latter stages of starvation. Men of all ages, were suffering the indignity of night blindness, causing them to flail their arms wildly as they trudged in the darkness. No help came from either the guards or from Kazik; whereas at one time he would have offered his support, now he did nothing, knowing it was pointless. It was only a matter of time before death came to these '*dokhodyagi*' (living dead) as they were officially known.

He found it immensely disturbing to see their final hours as they scavenged on the rubbish heaps, reduced to mere skeletons with shaven heads and inhuman faces. He found it unbearable to watch as they lost not just their minds but their entire self-respect, no longer having control of their bladder or bowel. Worse still, to add to their torment, kitchen staff would bait them, simply for their own amusement.

'Here you are,' some of the cooks would call, as they threw soup in their faces. It brought no reaction from the 'wicks', as they were nicknamed, who in their trance-like state were beyond caring.

Kazik reacted with a mixture of pity and despair. In his pity, he had once considered sharing his *paika* – his bread portion – with a fellow prisoner but he had quickly discovered the unwritten rule that this was neither acceptable nor expected. In his despair, he recognised these '*dokhodyagi*' were totally anonymous after they died. They were merely thrown into a mass grave, completely naked and simply forgotten. But what could he do to help? Nothing, simply nothing - except be forever determined not to become one of them.

He realised, if he were to die in this way, none of his family would be informed and certainly no-one would ever know if or where he was buried. With such an awful prospect, Kazik summoned all his will power and focused on finding any solution to his persistent hunger. In the days that followed, whilst working in the open, he spotted a field with a crop of newly- grown wheat. Whenever possible, he manoeuvred himself to the edge of his working party and hastily picked some of the young shoots, relishing the taste despite their inability to stave off the gnawing pain within his stomach.

Soon he was laid low by bouts of dysentery. A frequent trip to the overflowing latrines, where the stench was indescribable, was a constant necessity, resulting in the loss of even more of his bodily strength. Then diarrhoea flowed from him unannounced and he was unable to make it to the toilet in time. It scared him too when blood made its appearance, fearing how much longer he could survive. Despite this, he was still expected to complete his 'norm' every day. What a deliberately cunning way for the Soviets to gain total control, Kazik mused. The overwhelming desire for food was such a powerful motivator, most endeavoured to work hard, despite the torture of hunger and utter fatigue. But for how much longer could they continue these relentless work assignments, day after day, whatever the conditions?

As the weeks moved into autumn, the deteriorating weather brought more hardship. As the temperature plummeted, the prisoners grumbled – how could they be expected to survive with such inadequate clothing; rags rather than socks to wrap around their feet, felt shoes that weren't water proof and not enough winter jackets and padded trousers to go around. No wonder fights were breaking out and even disputes over underwear. Didn't every human being deserve underwear and yet Kazik witnessed them become treasured items – causing people to steal or gamble or worse... One evening in camp, a prisoner suddenly collapsed and dropped down dead. Within seconds, there was a commotion as individuals set upon his body. Instead of being treated with dignity, he was stripped of all his clothes and left where he lay, totally degraded.

In his head, Kazik found such behaviour shameful but again he repressed the images within his subconscious -as he had done with all the other horrors – not realising the damage they would cause his mind in the future. He had been brought up to be a decent person, someone with high morals who acted intelligently and treated others with respect. Now it seemed that everyone was living for themselves without pity or conscience. Must he harden himself and betray the beliefs that had been instilled into him since early childhood? Had the inmates all gone mad? In fact was he succumbing to insanity himself?

It was becoming increasingly common for prisoners to feign illness, hoping to secure a few days' respite from their daily grind. He watched as numerous deceits were tried: fake insanity, paralysis and infection, mainly brought about by rubbing unsavoury items into wounds. Some attempted to escape en-route to work but invariably they were caught by a team of horse-mounted guards and retribution quickly followed. The most unfortunate ones were immediately executed whilst the luckiest had their sentence extended. For others, it was the renowned 'punishment by mosquitoes' which was so horrific, all the other prisoners were forced to witness it as a deterrent. The offender, after being stripped naked, was hung crucifixion- style to a pine tree and left to the mercy of hundreds of blood sucking mosquitoes for half an hour or more. Inevitably, this resulted in a lingering, agonizing death.

A few prisoners, so desperate to find release from their intolerable suffering, decided to commit suicide. Kazik didn't want to consider this option but how could he continue? Every hour of every day, he yearned for something to happen to release him from this Soviet tyranny. He was despairing –would he ever be able to return home to his loving family and maybe marry in the future?

The mental torment of not knowing if release would ever come was almost the hardest thing to bear. As time passed and weeks of captivity turned to months, it seemed an impossible dream. As a Catholic he clung to his faith and belief in God. He tried to maintain hope yet his mind was constantly filled with dark thoughts and he wondered how much longer his human body could withstand extreme starvation and debilitating illness. He had almost come to believe that this incarceration was going to be permanent at least he knew that's what the NKVD wanted them to believe. Not knowing what the future held and the fear of what it might be had the worst possible effect on everyone's mood.....

CHAPTER 8
SCOTLAND   DECEMBER 1948

As the days moved further into December, things didn't improve regarding Kazik's general mood and Maria was constantly aware of his depressed state of mind. He still managed to go to work but on his return, he often chose to sit by the fire for the entire evening, staring blankly into the flames, lost in his own train of thought.

'Are you thinking of your imprisonment in Russia?' Maria asked one evening, trying to encourage him to speak to her. She thought if he shared some of his experiences, it might release him from some of his 'demons'.

Kazik stared ahead, looking beyond her and remaining unresponsive. What could she do? Maria was at a loss and felt alone in her anxiety. On occasions Seweryn would call round with his wife and their new baby boy and for a while Kazik relaxed as they chatted in Polish, recalling happy memories of their homeland and enjoying a game of bridge. But after they left, he returned to his melancholic state.

Maria found it genuinely hard to reconcile this despondent behaviour with the seemingly assured and approachable man she thought she had married. Yes, she understood he had a festering hatred for everything Russian, plus she accepted he was home sick but surely it was time to move on and not allow this misery to consume him? She considered they were better off living in Britain than hankering after their recent former way of life. She'd had to make huge adjustments after her trauma in Poland but she was determined her ordeal wouldn't overwhelm her.

'Can't you be happy living here as a free man? ' she asked in a moment of frustration.

Kazik continued to maintain his blank expression but she was equally determined to illicit an answer. She decided to adopt a different approach.

'Are you unhappy that you've married me?' she suggested rather pointedly.

Without warning, he jumped up from his chair and marched straight over in her direction. For a moment she recoiled, convinced he was about to hit her. She could almost feel his anguish, as well as seeing it in his face. He came close, his eyes fixed and glaring.

'Leave it!' he hissed, pushing past her and storming out of the house. It alarmed Maria to witness her husband's disturbed mood but she decided the best option was to leave him to cool down outside.

Afterwards, no reference was made to the incident. Kazik behaved as if nothing had happened whereas Maria was disturbed and began to question herself. Was it her fault that he had become so angry, although it seemed such an innocuous remark she had made. Maybe she had rather pressed him into reacting, yet she hated the thought of always having to mind what she said.   She was desperate for their relationship to work, wanting a partnership where they could share everything. They had both gone through so much and now they needed to rebuild their lives together, not destroy their relationship.

She hoped, yet again, that this outburst was just a one off but vowed to be more careful in future and not antagonise him. Yet it wasn't always easy to know what might cause him to over-react. On returning from work one winter evening, Kazik spotted an envelope on the mantel piece awaiting postage. It was in his wife's handwriting and bound for an address in London. Maria had simply written to a friend and was intending to post it the following morning. Unfortunately, it immediately aroused her husband's suspicion.

Grabbing the letter and wafting it in her face, he confronted her, 'Why are you writing to the Russian Ambassador in London?' he shouted accusingly.

'You've got it all wrong,' Maria explained, 'I'm writing to the Polish family that I stayed with in London when I first arrived in Britain.'

Kazik wouldn't listen. 'The Russians are determined to have me killed,' he reiterated.

Maria, frustrated by his accusations, snatched the envelope back and tore it open.

'Look! See! Read it – it's to a friend,' she said, almost shouting in her annoyance.

Again Kazik retreated outside, only returning much later, without even mentioning it.

Maria found herself becoming ever more fearful, scared of what might or might not trigger another eruption. What was she to do? She concluded there was nothing to be done but accept the situation with resilience, just as she had learnt to do with everything that life had thrown at her.

Instead, she would focus on Christmas – their first Christmas together. A festival which Kazik had always said he'd enjoyed in the past. It would not be quite the same this year, with no family around but it would be a wonderful chance to celebrate *Wigilia,* the Polish equivalent of Christmas Eve with lots of Polish food and drink. She could possibly invite the Novaks.

She decided to make the most of it. She wrote a few cards to friends, put up a real Christmas tree and decorated it with traditional red candles, the ones that needed to be clipped on. Hopefully, she thought, it might just focus Kazik's mind on happier times.

When some post dropped through the letter box, Maria picked it up with some excitement. Could it include a first Christmas card to them as a couple? One envelope immediately grabbed her attention – it looked too official to be a Christmas greeting, for the address label was typed and it was clearly marked 'For the attention of Mr Kazimierz Szwabowicz.'

Suddenly, Maria felt alarmed. On closer inspection, the postmark revealed that the letter had come all the way from Russia. Her heart began to race as she went through various scenarios in her head. What could the contents be regarding? More to the point, what would Kazik make of it? Just seeing the Russian postmark might lead him into believing all his delusions were correct and that the Russians were truly after him. That would be disastrous.

Conversely, the letter might be regarding his demobilisation from the army with instructions about returning to Poland in the future. That would undoubtedly give him some much needed hope. What a decision she had to make. Would it be best if she simply discarded the letter, without showing it to her husband?

After much consideration, she decided this was not a viable option concerned the letter might contain important documentation. She must show Kazik but she would need to choose her moment carefully. The following evening, after they'd eaten one of Kazik's favourite Polish meals, he went, as usual, to sit in his armchair in front of the fire. He was more talkative than of late, even asking how her day had gone. Maria decided this was her opportunity.

'Kazik, there's a letter arrived for you..... with a Russian post mark,' she said, waiting nervously to see how he would react.

Puzzled, he took it from her and stared down at the writing, for what seemed an eternity. In her head Maria was willing him to open it, but she held her silence.

Finally, he tore the envelope open. For Kazik, it was most unusual to receive correspondence written in his mother tongue and he immediately turned it over, looking to see the sender's identity. He took a sharp intake of breath.

'It's from the International Red Cross,' he explained.

'Why are they writing to you?' Maria asked, puckering her brow in surprise.

'Give me time to read it first!' he replied.

He scrutinised the correspondence front to back, then turned it over, re- read it, without uttering a word.

'What is it?' 'What is it?' asked Maria impatiently, as she studied his face, trying to gauge the reaction to its contents.

Eventually he spoke, slowly at first, trying to take in the enormity of what he'd read.

'They're telling me that my relations are searching for me. They're really keen to make contact. It's my sister Eugenia – the one arrested at the same time as me - she has made the initial enquiry. She must have contacted the Red Cross and asked them for help to try and trace me. I guess the Red Cross have been in touch with the Polish Resettlement Corps to access my details. Now they want to know whether I wish to be back in touch with my family. I have to write back and confirm if I do.'

'Kazik, that's wonderful, wonderful news, isn't it?' she asked rather tentatively, unable to gauge his response. Was he as excited as she thought he should be?

'Surely it means … it means … at least some of your family are still alive! You must reply immediately,' Maria suggested but her husband made no comment.

Over the following days, Kazik's initial enthusiasm appeared to become more muted. After mulling it over, he shared his thoughts with Maria.

'If I do make contact with my family, what do I say? How can I tell them that the chances of being reunited are very slim? You know I'll never be allowed to return to Poland whilst Josef Stalin and the communists are ruling our country. There's no way either that they'll ever be able to afford to come to Britain to visit us.'

Maria tried to be sympathetic but as always she took the more positive view.

'I understand what you are saying but at least you now know that Eugenia is alive and safe and maybe others so surely you want them to hear that you've survived too. Why don't you give the Red Cross an affirmative answer? I'll write to them on your behalf if you like.'

Kazik nodded, 'Yes they deserve to know but not just yet, first I need to be settled in my mind,' he explained, hoping Maria would accept his decision.

In truth, although he couldn't verbalise it, his heart was breaking. The thought of never seeing his next of kin or his homeland ever again was unbearable and the turmoil this created constantly troubled him. He really didn't feel settled in Britain and doubted if he ever would. He just couldn't get used to the British way of life. It wasn't just the food or the weather that didn't suit nor the ongoing problem of mastering the language, was it more that he was convinced the British people didn't like him and resented his presence. He felt trapped in a country where he believed he didn't belong but how could he escape?

Maria, on the other hand, tried to be more hopeful about her future in Britain. She had come to terms with her present life and liked to believe the local residents had accepted her. Besides, she wondered if Kazik realised how fortunate he was to have this breakthrough – if only she had the same hope to cling on to.

She really trusted, with the passing of time, this news of his family's survival would eventually encourage rather than discourage her husband. But even she had to admit she had her doubts. Was Kazik possibly correct in his assumptions that returning home was almost impossible? Had the Second World War really created a situation in which many Polish exiles were now banned from parts of Poland? She really hoped not. For, if that was the case, it was such an injustice and an utter betrayal by their so-called Allies. She knew what invaluable help the Poles, including her own husband, had given to the British forces in their fight against Germany. Even the Russians, she recalled, had turned to the Poles for help in 1941 when they realised the Germans were advancing on Moscow and beyond...

CHAPTER 9
RUSSIA - 1941

In September 1941, some startling news was beginning to filter through to the inmates of Ryazan camp, news which was greeted with a mixture of shock and disbelief. Could what they were hearing really be true? Had Stalin actually agreed to release them? Just what would prompt him to do this, the prisoners were debating or was it a false promise to further undermine their morale?

To put an end to all the rumours, one of the guards explained, 'The German army are continuing to advance into Russia and Stalin has realised he needs more foreign aid so he's turned to Poland for military help. To encourage your support, he's signed a truce, re-establishing diplomatic relations between Poland and Russia, and he's even declared an amnesty: '**for all Polish citizens, on the territory of the USSR who are at present deprived of their freedom, as prisoners of war.**'

The prisoners stared blankly at each other, trying to understand the full significance of this announcement.

'Does this truce mean Poland will regain its independence? Will the Soviets return all the land they've taken from us?' some of the more savvy inmates were keen to know.

Kazik was listening intently, eager as anyone to hear the answers.

'Such issues as border disputes haven't been discussed yet,' came the diplomatic reply.

Some prisoners reacted angrily, feeling the injustice of the agreement.

'Amnesty, Amnesty! How dare the Soviets use that word? We are innocent people who are to be set free, not people who are to be let off from their crimes.'

'Let it go,' other suggested, 'it's not the time to quibble over words, surely the best news is that we are to be released.'

'How long will we have to wait though?' some asked, others showed no response, being too physically weak to care or too mentally ill to understand the implications.

Secretly Kazik had many pertinent questions on his mind but he wasn't prepared to verbalise them. His main concern was the effect this amnesty might have on his future. Would it be possible to return to Poland or would his home village – Zupran- continue to be under Russian control? He had fears on a basic level too for he would need to find employment and that had been an issue for him, even before this incarceration. Now he was a mere shadow of himself, wasted away, struggling with his bowels and bearing the weight of deep mental scars.

'I hear there's talk of a Polish army being established on Soviet territory,' one of the prisoners announced a few days later, after overhearing the guards speak of it. 'They even suggest that General Wladyslaw Anders might be   appointed to command this new army.'

This truly interested Kazik. A role in the army might just be what he needed. As for General Anders, he'd known him to be a Polish officer who had   been a prisoner of war himself, incarcerated by the Russians for many months, accused of being a German spy. As such, he had earned great respect from many Poles.

'I'm sure Anders hates the Russians as much as we do,' one prisoner commented, 'I would be pleased to have the opportunity to fight under his command. He would be a great asset to the Polish cause.'

Many nodded their heads in agreement.

'But where will we find this army?' other prisoners asked, fearing it was all hearsay.

'Maybe we'll have to hitch hike around the Soviet Union until we find it.'

'That's a huge task,' one elderly prisoner suggested, realising it was quite beyond his physical capabilities.

Kazik agreed. Recognising how unfit most of them were, he doubted if many would be considered for enrolment, even if they managed to locate the right destination.

'Do we really think we will be safe in Russia?' a young man questioned, feeling fearful that Stalin was not to be trusted.

'But what choice do we have?' others interjected, 'Let's just see what happens and try to stay positive. We're going to be free, aren't we?'

The majority agreed but all were struggling. On a practical level alone, it seemed a huge undertaking, when almost everyone was at the limit of their endurance.

Over the following days, the food rations certainly began to improve which was a real morale booster. It was such a joy to receive their full quota, irrespective of whether they fulfilled their 'norm' or not.

Next, an assignment of fresh clothes brought added comfort. Some prisoners, whilst pleased with this new upturn in their fortune, held a cynical attitude, summed up by one elderly inmate.

'I guess Josef Stalin is worried. Worried what stories we might tell the world, once we are away from the NKVD's clutches,' he suggested as he devoured his extra portion of bread.

Others remained silent – frightened to say anything in case it could lead to reprisals. Whilst for a few, the news of possible release came too late, as every day someone in the camp died and although it no longer merited any attention, Kazik felt the injustice of it. How awful that so many fellow Poles should die, just as they were on the very threshold of a new life. He looked down at his own emaciated body and felt he'd grown old. His incarceration had been barely six months yet it felt like years.

Later that week, after morning roll call, one of the main guards appeared nervous as he stood to deliver an important announcement, knowing it was likely to provoke a strong reaction.

'Orders have been sent through from headquarters that all prisoners in this Soviet labour camp are to be released from captivity on the 13th of September ....You must now put your differences aside and fight our common enemy – Germany.'

The tension in the air was tangible. The men's faces were pained as they shook their heads in disbelief, inwardly raging over this command. Put their differences aside! These particular words thundered in Kazik's head. For months all of them had been severely ill- treated, he had witnessed so many prisoners reduced to mere skeletons and even more to corpses. How could they possibly forget their ordeal and behave as if nothing had happened? They might be glad to fight the Germans but to work alongside the Red Army as a united front was surely an impossible ask.

The guard, ignoring their obvious discontent, simply continued.

'Each prisoner is to be given a rail travel certificate in lieu of a passport, to a destination of their choice which will be valid for three months.'

Many, including Kazik, felt totally bemused at the vagueness of this information, having no true idea where they would want the rail certificate to take them. Where would they find this army that they had heard much talk about?

'Where are we to go?' the braver ones asked.

'I suggest you travel southwards, across the Soviet Union to Kazakhstan. On the way, scattered across the country, you will find army collection centres where you can gain further assistance and food,' one of the more humane guards explained and left it at that.

The prisoners were stunned but in the end most of them decided that joining the army was maybe the best option or indeed the only option. Yes, they would be travelling into an unknown future but a military path would surely offer them a degree of both protection and fulfilment.

When release day arrived, the prisoners lined up for the final time. It seemed almost surreal; after being handed a subsistence of one hundred roubles plus a stamp to allow use of a general store for a week, they were free to walk out of the camp gates.

Nobody showed any real enthusiasm as they left. They simply became an endless stream of weary people, all with little aim except to find a train station. They each carried the barest of travel items yet to outsiders they seemed weighed down. Their bodies appeared stooped and twisted; their faces were lifeless and shapeless whilst their ragged clothes barely covered them. Some had sticks to lean on but most were hobbling, with their feet covered in either newspaper or dirty cloth, tied with string. A few were even barefoot. They had barely the energy to place one foot in front of another.

There was little chatter amongst them, most felt too traumatised or too ill to talk. Kazik trudged along with the rest, eventually locating a train station only to watch as train after train, already crowded with Poles, simply passed by.

'We're no better off than in the camp,' many grumbled as the hours passed by and they hadn't eaten or drank.

Finally, a train stopped. Everyone crowded on board. It travelled southwards to where they all hoped true freedom would be found but the following days were harsh. Hunger and thirst continued to be an issue and illness was rife. Kazik constantly struggled with dysentery and was disappointed to find conditions on the train little improvement to those he'd endured on the cattle trucks, several months earlier. Once again the carriages were crammed beyond capacity and sanitary conditions were simply appalling. At least though, there were regular stops at certain stations with kiosks where bread, boiled water and occasionally soup were handed out.

For much of the endless journey he sat deep in thought, staring out of the window as the train headed away from the industrial heartland of Russia into the arid steppes of northern Kazakhstan. Suddenly his deliberations were interrupted as noise levels rose in the carriage. He looked up to see men conversing eagerly with each other. He strained to hear their conversation.

'I've heard we are to travel to Guzar in Uzbekistan, if we want to be recruited into the Polish army.'

This news travelled fast throughout the train. Was it true? Had they finally discovered where they needed to be?

Progress however, continued to be slow, frequently they were shunted into sidings whilst higher priority Russian military transport was allowed to pass. At every station, many more exiles boarded the train. Gradually, the carriages became so overcrowded that some prisoners even resorted to travelling on the roof, despite its obvious danger.

When the train finally arrived at the city of Guzar, thousands of army hopefuls disembarked. They were marched out of the town to a large military camp, surrounded by a high barbed wire fence. Instead of being alarmed by the sight, Kazik was thrilled. For there, over the entrance to the camp, flew the red and white flag of Poland. At last he felt there was hope – was he truly a free man now?

After showing the guards his official Soviet release document, his details were registered and the inevitable medical examination followed. It felt immensely comforting to be treated with genuine   compassion and understanding by the doctors who seemed truly shocked by what they were seeing. To them, all the volunteers looked practically identical. Each one was painfully thin, with bones protruding from sagging skin. Their faces were either gaunt or bloated and their eyes, sunken within their bearded faces, had lost their lustre, seemingly devoid of personality. Some could barely stand and a desperate few were so traumatised they could only grunt. Yet all showed a determination and eagerness to sign up.

The doctor's next words took Kazik by surprise,   'Fit - Category A. '

What a relief. Now he considered himself a true soldier and was pleased to be assigned to the artillery training section. He was allocated into a group of ten men who were directed to their own tent.

All the men were more than ready for a meal, feeling immensely grateful when orders came to queue up outside the kitchen, where soup was to be served. This time, the line was patient, with everyone waiting in turn for soup that was actually edible, tasty even and it was wonderful.

Next, came the delights of a comforting warm bath and a full shave, after which every man was escorted to the quartermaster's store and given a Polish army uniform, a kitbag and a warm blanket. Many soldiers were overcome with emotion. On opening their kitbag, they spotted a bowl and spoon and were instantly reminded of their captivity. Many were tempted to conceal them away but then realised it wasn't necessary.

Kazik was silent as he drew the blanket to his face, it felt warm to the touch and he delighted in its fresh smell. He picked up the uniform and realised this was a redefining moment. He had survived whilst thousands of his fellow Poles had not, so he must, he told himself, draw on his inner strength and continue to remain positive for the future.

Over the following days, he began to relax, knowing that proper wholesome food was readily available. Also, for the first time he started to converse with the other men in his tent, without having to worry that an informer might be present. He even enjoyed playing bridge or having a proper game of cards.

'Things are looking up for us,' commented one of his groups.

'Although I don't really think we're quite up to military standards,' another laughed as he looked at the physical state of his fellow men, all of them shockingly underweight and feeling perpetually exhausted.

'Perhaps we'll even get back to Poland by the end of the year,' someone else suggested, trying to be encouraging.

Kazik was not so sure but he said nothing. He felt certain that whilst they continued to be trapped inside Russia, there would never be a chance to return home.

Then, quite unexpectedly, some exciting news began to filter through the camp.

'The Russians have decided to let us go. We can leave the country,' an officer explained.

'What, how come?' one man asked, rather taken aback by this turn around. It was so unlike the Soviet Union to agree to such terms.

'Apparently, Stalin has changed his mind about having a Polish army on Russian soil. He's agreed to let our army come under the control of the British so now they're willing to evacuate us.'

'Where do you think we'll be going?' the spokesman of the party asked.

'Could it possibly mean a return to Poland?' enquired a chorus of eager voices, only to be let down by their commanding officer.

'No lads, I'm sorry it's not. We're to be re-located to the Middle East. On arrival, we will all be trained, equipped and deployed to help protect the key oil fields in the southern Caucasus in the event of a German attack.'

Disappointed but not totally deflated, the men were grateful that at least they were escaping the Soviet Union. Kazik and his fellow prisoners were then instructed to gather together all their belongings and dismantle their tents. The evacuation from Russia had begun. With all their possessions strapped to their backs, they assembled in readiness to be marched to waiting trains. They'd been informed that they were heading westwards, destined for the Caspian Sea port of Kransovodsk for embarkation to the Persian port of Pahlevi.

On their arrival at Kransovodsk, the queue waiting for evacuation was immense – not just soldiers but groups of civilians including women and children.

'If you have any Russian money with you, you must place it in these crates as you board the ship,' all the waiting evacuees were told.

'They're not having my paper money,' some argued and they disappeared into the latrines to use it for an alternative purpose.

As the thronging crowd walked up to the gangplank, the passengers became unruly, pushing each other in their eagerness to get on board. The fear of being left behind was enormous – the prospect of staying in Russia was unthinkable. However the ship certainly wasn't designed to take so many people and soon it was heaving. Kazik was just glad to find a space to lay down his kit bag and squat against it.

After several hours of sailing, the boat suddenly came to a juddering halt. The shoreline was within sight but the ship remained stationary whilst the crunching sound of her anchor chain being lowered, reverberated around the deck.

'What's happening? We're not about to turn back are we?' an anxious passenger remarked.

'The captain is frightened that the boat might run aground at the harbour entrance. If that happens, he knows full well what the Russians would do to him,' one of the civilians explained.

'I'm going to swim ashore!' a desperate man shouted as he jumped into the rough sea.

Anxious passengers watched as he initially flailed around in the water. Fortunately, he proved to be a strong swimmer and he appeared to reach the shore. For the rest of the evacuees, the wait seemed endless but eventually cargo boats arrived to carry them all to land. Once ashore many chose to pray, offering thanks to God that freedom was theirs at last. No longer were they under Russian jurisdiction as Persia was British controlled and reassuringly, this surely meant recuperation with better treatment.

'We have army trucks waiting to take you to a transit camp where you will be given food and shelter,' a British official explained.

Along the way, the trucks were besieged by the local inhabitants who ran eagerly towards the vehicles; everyone was instantly struck by the warmth and friendliness of the Persians. Without hesitation, both men and women crowded around, offering not only shouts of welcome but gifts of food – including pomegranates, raisins, figs, dates and nuts. Kazik surveyed the delicacies, feeling in total awe at the abundance and variety that was on offer to him, such a stark contrast to what he'd been given in recent weeks. Reluctantly, he declined their kindness, in fear of the effect on his shrunken stomach. He doubted if he would be able to tolerate anything remotely rich or fatty. So instead he smiled politely and nodded his head as an acknowledgment of their generosity.

After a short journey, the prisoners finally arrived at the camp and Kazik was instantly struck by the thousands of tents which stretched for several miles along the beach, all in neat rows, marked by white painted stones. There were also many out-buildings including latrines, bath houses, laundry facilities, and even a post office and shops. But perhaps, most importantly, there was a hospital.

In fact, the first stop for all the new arrivals was the medical reception compound where they had to wait to be assessed. When

Kazik's name was called, he was understandably surprised to come face to face with armed guards. He understood they posed no threat but he still felt vulnerable. Would he pass this preliminary hurdle? First came a check -up of his ears, eyes, nose and throat but fortunately there was no intrusive probing or intimate examination. Then he heard the welcome command, 'Report to the 'clean area', realising it meant he wouldn't need to be quarantined.

Next on the agenda was a shower and ablutions. The warmth of the clear water felt liberating on his tired body and oh the luxury of a bar of fresh soap. Even the full shave and delousing seemed pleasurable, finally ridding him of the dreaded lice. His mood was further lifted with the allocation of new clothes that were not only dry and clean but actually fitted him. Included was a helmet decorated with the Polish eagle. After dressing, he looked down at himself with pride. It was a good feeling to be wearing an army uniform once again. Little did he know it but the day – 1st April 1942- was also his first entry on his Polish army record.

Just days later, news quickly filtered through the ranks that General Anders had arrived, with the intention of examining his new 'army'. This time, on command, all the men lined up without complaint. Anders was deeply shocked by the men's poor state of health and their lack of appropriate weapons. In his head, he was wondering if it would be possible to make a fighting combat force with such an undernourished, impoverished group yet he was instantly impressed by their obvious fervour and their complete solidarity. But he knew that there was some rather difficult advice he needed to give them. Just how would they take it? He cleared his throat and paused before uttering some historic words.

'The time has come to forget about the injustice and the suffering you have endured so far.'

Then he faltered for he recognised the need to temper this statement with words of encouragement.

'Now your main goal is to fight for a free Poland... however long it takes.'

At first Ander's order made Kazik feel a degree of anger and resentment. How could he ever forget the injustice of his imprisonment when he had been innocent of any crime? Why should he not remember all the atrocities that the Russians had meted out? In fact they had become indelibly written in his mind. He may have been released from captivity but there was no escaping the daily torment of the horrors he had witnessed...... indeed would he ever be free of these images in the future?

70

Yet Ander's wanted them to focus on freeing Poland and this was surely worth consideration. Maybe this new army would provide the opportunity to fight for justice, avenge all the many wrongs committed by the Soviet Union and even restore Poland's independence. To think he could play his part in that provided an alternative to his anger. At that moment he felt proud to be a Szwabowicz, and was sure his father would have been delighted at this stance he was making to help Poland regain its freedom.

General Anders was proving to be a wise man and he understood that many of the men were harbouring a deep resentment towards their Russian captors and finding the concept of becoming their allies, extremely difficult. He had devised a possible solution which he hoped would help the prisoners release some of their antagonism and allow them to put disturbing memories behind them. He had it in mind to individually record their treatment by the Russians.

'Can I encourage you all to give me a hand written statement about where you were imprisoned geographically plus the horrific living conditions you had to endure.'

Kazik responded positively to this suggestion. Over the following days, he wrote down details regarding the appalling conditions within the prison at Stara Wilejka and the labour camp at Ryazan. He accepted it was cathartic to write down something of this ordeal but equally there were many horrors he just could not record. There were things he'd witnessed that had affected him profoundly and were deeply impregnated into his psyche but he didn't ever want to recall them, let alone write them down for others to read. How could he relate such atrocities as seeing a man garrotted with wire or babies thrown against …no, no, it was too brutal and too shocking for anyone to know of or even believe. The images would stay with him for ever but it would stay with him alone….

As Kazik handed over his completed account, he heard someone asking one of the officers a very pertinent question. 'What do you think might happen to all these documents? They will certainly contain much damning evidence of Stalin's cruel acts. Do you think they will be kept secret?'

'I'm not entirely sure,' the officer replied honestly, 'but I doubt it. I feel certain they will be locked away for now but one day they will be available for the world to read and then your innocence and bravery will surely be acknowledged.'*

*These accounts were released into the public domain many years later and a copy of Kazik's testimony was obtained from The Hoover Institute in USA.

These were comforting words and the soldiers felt even more pleased that they had had this opportunity. In time too, with exercise, drills and discipline, the whole company began to progress and show signs of becoming a more viable fighting force. The effect of regular, nourishing meals resulted in a vast improvement to everyone's general health and their level of stamina.

In the early months of 1943, the army were on their travels once more, destined for the new Polish army headquarters in Quizil-Ribat, Iraq. Immediately on his arrival, Kazik was struck by the intense heat. The men weren't expecting the huge tented army camp to be located in the desert where temperatures had been known to reach fifty degrees at midday.

'We'll roast like chickens!' someone commented.

'But then we'll be frozen chickens at night,' responded another, trying to raise a smile.

It was certainly a relief to all when the camp commander explained, 'You must be up early every morning and prepared for training. When the heat intensifies, you will then be able to stop and relax.'

Shortly after their arrival, the army was reorganised. Kazik was assigned to his first proper army unit - the 9th Field Artillery Regiment. The training that followed was tough and intensive, designed so that they could rapidly develop their military skills. He learnt to handle new weapons and was initiated into the latest methods of warfare. Additionally, he was delighted when, along with twenty thousand others, he was taught to drive, not just military motor cars but lorries and tractors as well. This was a completely new experience for him, indeed for most of the Poles who had solely   travelled by horse and cart back home.

Kazik was particularly pleased when he was chosen for further training in the role of sniper in which he could develop his love for map reading. He began to think that maybe he was accepted, valued even, which had been a very distant and alien feeling in recent years. There was also regular monitoring of his physical health which he accepted as positive rather than negative. Although he found himself living in a primitive tent, he realised it was a vast improvement to the months spent in those dreadful barracks. The only real problem he had to deal with was checking for snakes and scorpions that others warned him might stray into his bed. Surely things were looking up.

But as the months passed and the days moved into autumn, Kazik and his fellow soldiers were becoming understandably restless. For nearly two years they had endured a long, hard journey, covering thousands of miles over difficult terrain. They had been intensely trained and equipped ready for battle yet they still hadn't seen any military action, despite their obvious eagerness to fight. Visiting dignitaries had all remarked on their fearless spirit and enthusiasm and their devotion to the Polish cause. All the ex- prisoners desperately wanted a chance to regain their honour; a chance to not only fight the hated Germans but also to fulfil their deepest desire to see Poland free once more. So when some news came through to the camp that at last they had a purpose, it received a very warm reaction.

'The British Prime Minister, Winston Churchill, wants to send you all to Italy where there is an urgent need for reinforcements.... there you will come under the command of General Montgomery's 8th British Army, the well renowned 'desert rats' who are already fighting the Germans over there.'

But then there was an unexpected rider to this announcement. 'You are to be sent to Palestine first, in order to acclimatise you to the terrain and climate, being similar to the conditions you will experience in Italy,' the commander explained.

At first the soldiers were feeling slightly deflated by this but their dissatisfaction didn't last long. On their arrival at Gaza in Palestine, it seemed the accommodation was well organised, the weather extremely favourable and a great variety of food was on offer.

Kazik was further encouraged when his commander explained, 'This Polish army in the east is going to be renamed. You will now be known as the Second Polish Corps. It will adopt, as its insignia, a white design based on the coat of arms of Warsaw with a little mermaid on a red background- the national colours of Poland.'

This lifted his morale and all the troop's enthusiasm was back on track. As more equipment became available, their training stepped up a further gear which pleased everybody; such was their eagerness to be involved. For Kazik, it also brought promotion from corporal officer cadet to sergeant. Not long afterwards, further heartening news came through that the Italian army had surrendered in September. Surely, this was an encouraging sign that things were improving regarding their country's war with Germany.

One wintry morning in November, a Sherman tank suddenly arrived in the camp. News quickly spread that it was carrying General Sosnkowski, their new Polish Commander in Chief, as well as General Anders. The troops were summoned to listen as Sosnkowski, standing on top of the tank, announced, 'The Polish 2nd Army are now going to be travelling to Italy. It is what you have been waiting for, you will finally take part in the war for Europe. Then hopefully you will return to your homeland of Poland.'

Was this really true? Kazik didn't quite know how to respond. It was hard to imagine that he might possibly be able to return home the following year. He wanted to believe it but at the same time he was cautious. Over the next few months he would have to fight a real enemy and he had to face the possibility that he might not survive the final hurdle.

Yet he reminded himself it was almost Christmas, and he recalled just what that festival had meant to him and his family back home. They'd all loved *Wigilia* (Christmas Eve) and they had always gone to the Catholic church together every Christmas morning and enjoyed a wonderful meal afterwards. So instead of dwelling on the future, he concentrated on the present. He decided on Christmas Eve, to attend a Christmas Mass (*Pasterka*) in Bethlehem, along with thousands of other Polish soldiers.

Listening to the service in his native language was a truly special moment. Kazik stood in silence, his head bowed, acknowledging the fact that he was alive and safe. For a few precious moments, his mind wandered back to Zupran and his family. Were they all at home celebrating the birth of the Christ child, he wondered? Would they be standing round a tree, lit with real candles, maybe singing Silent Night? If they were indeed alive, no doubt they would be thinking of him too, especially his babunia. Was it possible that his sisters might be with them, having been freed and reunited with their other siblings? Could the New Year possibly be the time when he would finally re-join them? It seemed an impossible dream but at last he had some hope of its reality and that was a very good feeling.

CHAPTER 10
CHRISTMAS 1948 - HAMILTON, SCOTLAND

Christmas was approaching and both Maria and Kazik were really looking forward to it. Kazik loved this festival and this year was extra special, not simply because it was their first one together in their own 'home' but in recent times he'd believed so often, that he'd not live to celebrate it ever again.

With just two days to go, he had finished work for the holiday but was determined to keep himself active.

'I've offered to help a Polish friend with a few jobs, so I'll be out of the house for a while,' he explained.

'That's not a problem,' Maria replied smiling. She was grateful to have some time to herself, as she busied herself with the final preparation of all the festive food they both loved.

With him out of the house, she gathered together all the ingredients and utensils she would need and placed them on the kitchen table. There was the carp to prepare and set in jelly and the cheese to make with sour milk but first she decided, she would make a cake using her own recipe. She put the oven on to warm and looked at the clock, making a note of the time. Then, after putting on her cloth apron, she tossed some flour in the bowl and added the milk, eggs, sugar and butter.

Suddenly, as she began to stir, a persistently loud knock at the front door, interrupted her.

Maria tutted. What a time to get a visitor. Wiping her hands on the apron, she opened the door, hoping, whoever it was, wouldn't find any smudge of flour on her nose. Maria instantly recognised her caller as the wife of Kazik's friend.

'Come quickly! Come quickly! Your husband's had an accident,' the lady explained, speaking in Polish.

Alarmed, Maria switched off the oven, grabbed her coat and followed the woman down the street to her home. On her arrival, another neighbour approached Maria, 'The ambulance has already taken your husband to a hospital in Glasgow but transport has been arranged for you to follow him there.'

Maria nodded in appreciation, trying to maintain a calm exterior but understandably, she was feeling extremely concerned.

'What happened? What ever happened?' she asked the woman who had kindly agreed to accompany her.

Slowly, she built up a picture, although details were rather vague. It seemed Kazik and his friend had been enclosed in the garage, whilst filling a car with petrol. The friend had accidentally spilled some of it, which had then combusted, causing a minor explosion. The extent of Kazik's injuries was unclear but it seemed he had taken the brunt of it. His friend was shocked but uninjured. A torrent of thoughts rushed through Maria's mind. What would she find on her arrival at the ward? Had her husband been disfigured? Was his life in danger even?

Initially, when the doctors informed her of the severity of his burns, Maria became upset. Fortunately though it seemed it was the back of his legs that were affected rather than his face or upper body. The doctors tried to reassure her, explaining that although he may be scarred, his walking and such like would hopefully not be affected.

Maria was eager to see and speak to Kazik but she accepted that he was in a state of severe shock and understood when he seemed unresponsive. She looked down at his heavily bandaged legs and wondered just what his prospects were for a full recovery.

She returned home much later that day with a heavy heart. When she walked back into the house, there, facing her were all the cooking ingredients still on the table. She slowly put them away, realising there was absolutely no point in making any festive treats. Her husband wouldn't be home again for quite a while. Their first Christmas together was not going to happen. What a disappointment and what problems it presented.

Travelling to Glasgow every day to visit him was not only going to be costly but extremely difficult due to a lack of public transport over the holiday period. However, at that moment, she was just too weary to concern herself with such issues. She would face them tomorrow….

Over the next few days, Maria was pleased when Kazik's external injuries gradually began to heal but he seemed constantly anxious and melancholic whenever she manged to arrange a visit. She understood he was missing home and that he was in pain but was it more than that?

The doctors themselves began expressing concern over his mental state and they pulled Maria to one side.

'Have you noticed anything unusual about your husband's behaviour in recent weeks?'

Maria coloured up as she recalled the recent episodes where he had lost his temper over irrelevancies …..But were they worthy of mention?

She did explain that there had been incidences of irrational paranoia such as when he complained of being persecuted and hunted down by the Russians, even accusing her of being an accomplice in plots to kill him.

'But then he has been through traumatic times in recent years,' she added, in her desire to stay loyal to him, trying to justify his outbursts. 'He never wants to talk about his past but I know full well how badly it affected him.'

The doctors listened respectfully but as far as she was aware, nothing more was said or done on the matter. After just two weeks in hospital, the staff felt his injuries had improved enough for him to be allowed home to convalesce.

Kazik was delighted, he hated being in hospital, especially struggling as he did with communication due to his poor grasp of English. Maria was equally pleased to have her husband home, believing she was capable of looking after him and that he would recover more quickly in her care.

Both spoke of their sadness at missing out on their first Christmas together but it seemed incidental now. Besides, Maria had something important to share with him which mattered far more. Yet she was reluctant to tell him, fearing it might throw him off balance…

She waited patiently for a day or two, until her husband seemed more settled and had managed to control his levels of pain.

'I've intended to tell you something for a while but I wanted to be sure I was right in my assumptions,' she began.

'What is it?' Kazik interrupted, becoming rather agitated.

'Is it to do with my friend? I think you're going to tell me that he arranged the accident, intending to harm me, aren't you?'

Maria sighed. Why was he still dwelling on these ridiculous thoughts? Perhaps if he had better news to focus on then it might put an end to them.

'No, No Kazik. It's really good news,' she stressed, and then she paused. …. I'm having a baby –we will be parents by the end of August...'

The room went silent for a moment as Kazik processed the news.

'Is it true? Is it true?' he repeated, as his serious demeanour changed into a warm smile.

'Yes the doctor confirmed it, just this week,' Maria explained.

'Me – a father! That will take some getting used to ,' Kazik responded before adding wistfully, 'If only I could tell my family, my babunia would be so proud.'

Although he did seem genuinely pleased, his reaction over the following days was not as enthusiastic as Maria hoped it would be. She wasn't feeling too good herself in this early stage of pregnancy and certainly didn't want to be stressed by concerns over her husband. Yet sadly her fears for his state of mind became increasingly justified.

Throughout January, Kazik's mental state continued to deteriorate as exhaustion seemed to overwhelm him and he became totally self- absorbed. Unable to return to work, he confined himself to the house and withdrew from reality. He would sit staring into the fire for long periods. Unable to fall asleep, he often paced up and down during the night which Maria found particularly frustrating due to the negative impact on her own rest.

But what really alarmed her was when he seemed to lose the power to reason, becoming more deluded than ever. In his mind he saw abnormal things happening- he was convinced that objects in the house, such as towels, were moving. He imagined that shrouded figures were appearing before him and these images deeply troubled him.

'I need to visit the priest,' he explained to Maria one afternoon, 'as I seem to be seeing things that are most abnormal.'

The priest listened but was at a loss to know how to help. Instead he simply pacified Kazik by assuring him that the towels may well have moved.

The hallucinations continued and once more he became convinced that bad men were intent on poisoning him.

When Maria placed food in front of him, he pushed it aside.

'I'm not eating it,' he said angrily, 'it might contain poison.'

At first, Maria either ignored his behaviour or tried to humour him but then things came to a head.

One evening he began yet again with his tirade, insisting, 'The Russian police are out to get me. They want to kill me!'

'That's not true, no-one is after you,' Maria replied gently.

Suddenly, he jumped up from his chair and faced Maria full on. Glaring at her, he menacingly pointed his index finger, almost jabbing her in the face.

'And you, YOU are in league with them, I know you want to kill me too,' he shouted.

Maria tried to stay still and calm, this wasn't her husband talking, this was his sickness making him say and do things out of character.

'That's not true either, I assure you,' she reiterated, trying desperately to pacify him.

'It is! You and all the other people in this house, you are all out to get me.'

'Why would I want to get rid of you?' she asked, hoping he'd come to his senses.

'So that you can be with that married Pole of yours!' (referring to one of the other house inmates)

Maria was visibly shaking and shook her head in denial. Without warning, Kazik suddenly lunged forward and grabbed her by the throat.

'I'll kill you!' he threatened, as he held her tightly in his grip.

Alarmed, Maria resisted, struggling to free herself, as she felt herself fighting for breath.

'Kazik! What are you doing I'm pregnant with your child!' she gasped, hoping to placate him.

'No that's a lie,' he insisted, laughing out loud.

Tears welled in Maria's eyes, as she froze in terror. Kazik looked at his wife's reddened face, saw the fear in her eyes and slowly he began to compose himself. Within minutes, his anger appeared to have subsided and he was back to 'normal'.

'I'm so sorry. I don't know what came over me,' he blurted.

'You're ill, you are not thinking clearly,' Maria spoke quietly, trying to accept his apology but feeling seriously perturbed and with good cause.

Further outbursts followed and once again, in one of his flare ups, he physically assaulted her. Maria realised this latest behaviour had overstepped the mark and she became increasingly anxious that he might really harm her or worse still, their unborn child. What was she to do? Where could she turn for help? It wasn't the sort of issue to be shared with friends or neighbours and there were no family members to confide in. Her greatest desire was to be happy with Kazik but she found it so hard to understand what was happening. When he acted normally, he was considerate, loving even but he had become such a different person of late. In fact, she was becoming increasingly fearful of what the future might hold.

Were all those years of suffering deeply affecting his mind? Or was he intensely angry because of the outcome of the war? Nobody could blame him for being so irate.

She knew he'd joined the army with a hope and determination that Poland might regain its independence yet such a dream had proved futile. Certainly they'd been let down by their western allies in numerous ways, especially after the war. The appalling way the Poles had been treated, especially by the British, could only be described as a complete betrayal .....

CHAPTER 11
1944 - THE JOURNEY TO ITALY

It was early February and the troops of the Polish 2nd Corps were pleased that finally, they were on their way to combat. They were moving to Alexandria, the largest of the Egyptian sea ports, to be boarded onto a fleet of Allied ships which would transport them to southern Italy.

Thousands of them, all with their equipment, needed to be safely installed but they were orderly and patient, for they were feeling in euphoric mood. To be a combat force at last, was a great feeling. It was also reassuring to spot some Polish cruisers and submarines, preparing to protect their route along the coast of North Africa.

The journey proved difficult for Kazik and his fellow passengers as the ship tossed around in the raging waters, causing many to become sea sick. There came a great sense of relief when four days later, the coastal city of Taranto was spotted and they could set foot back on dry land.

Conditions though, weren't quite what they had imagined. As they moved up north through this mountainous region, ready to face the front line on the River Sangro, the weather really deteriorated. It was becoming bitterly cold, with snow on the high ground whilst underfoot it was wet and muddy. The men certainly appreciated their warm clothing and the benefits of being well fed, so in contrast to conditions during their prison days. Fortunately, military action was light, with just a few minor raids on German positions, so time was spent exercising.

In mid- March, their attention was temporarily side-tracked by a catastrophic event happening near Naples. Mount Vesuvius had suffered its worst eruption for two hundred years and it was reported that a whole town – San Sebastiano – had been virtually obliterated by molten lava. There was much talk of a huge cloud of smoke, almost three miles high that was depositing ash over a large area, ruining crops and even causing several fatalities from asphyxiation.

But by April, General Anders had some significant news of his own to share with his troops. The British Prime Minister, Winston Churchill, wanted the Polish 2nd Corps to take responsibility for breaking through a German defence line, known as the Curzon Line, near the town of Monte Cassino. He needed them to capture the historic Benedictine abbey, which stood on Monastery Hill, as German paratroopers were strategically placed there, providing them with an excellent defensive position.

The British 8th army had already carried out three assaults in this area, assisted by heavy bombing, but despite their best efforts, the German defence line had not been penetrated. They had succeeded in destroying the abbey but the paratroopers still occupied the ruins and were monitoring every movement by the Allies in the valley below. As for the British troops, they were totally exhausted as well as depleted in number.

Anders readily accepted this challenge, realising this venture wouldn't just be an opportunity to put his troop's newly acquired skills into action, hopefully it would mean a chance to bring Poland's cause to the attention of the world.

Speaking with great emotion before the planned fourth assault on May 11th, Anders knew exactly how all the ex - prisoners were feeling and he hoped his powerful words would challenge his troops to respond.

'Soldiers, the task assigned to us will cover with glory the name of the Polish soldier all over the world. The moment for battle has arrived. At this moment the thoughts and hearts of our whole nation will be with us. We have long awaited the moment for revenge and retribution over our hereditary enemy. For this action, let the lion spirit enter your hearts, keep deep in your heart God, honour and our land Poland. Go and take revenge for all the suffering in our land, for what you have suffered for many years and for years of separation from your families.'

The words certainly resonated deeply with Kazik. Feeling completely determined and empowered, he along with his fellow soldiers began marching upwards towards the hill, under the cover of darkness. With their faces and equipment blackened, they walked in their camouflage wraps, maintaining complete silence. They were playing a major role and how they knew it. If they could only take the abbey and penetrate the German defences, it would secure the opening of the road to Rome and surely lead to the ultimate conquest of Italy, fundamentally helping to win the war.

As he made the ascent, Kazik could just pick out in the moon-light, some horrific reminders of the past four months of battle. The trees, once vibrant with life, were now simple black posts, stripped of leaves and form. The grass, once a carpet underfoot, was now non-existent, replaced by waterlogged craters full of wet, slimy mud. But worst of all, were the ghostly shapes of disfigured bodies, in different stages of decay. A suffocating odour hung in the air and added to the gloom.

The attack was scheduled for eleven o' clock and the men, along with a massive artillery barrage, lined up along the entire front, waiting for the signal. It was deafening as the guns finally roared into action, as they began to pound the German artillery positions. Unfortunately, they were working virtually blind as the mountain side was so steep; the German positions couldn't be identified. The Germans had been clever too, ensuring they were well protected in their deep, concrete reinforced bunkers. They immediately responded with smoke launchers which fired mortar shells six at a time. A Polish soldier soon had them nick named.

'Watch out for the 'roaring cows',' he warned, on catching the first sound of their distinctive whining noise.

The fighting continued throughout the next day, some of it hand to hand and the German shells were unremitting. After huge losses of life, the Polish troops were forced to retreat as evening arrived. General Anders was visibly distressed and the troops were drained – physically and psychologically – but Brigadier General Oliver Leese, the commander of the 8th British army, was eager to reassure them.

'You have been of great assistance, for by tying up German defenders, you have assisted the British troops in the valley below.'

But then came shattering news. The Germans had retaliated in the most inhuman way imaginable. They had captured two young Polish officer cadets and crucified them. This atrocity simply fired up the troops and now they were resolute, determined to gain revenge with a further attack. They had such an intense, blind hatred for the Germans, they would stop at nothing to achieve success.

'We have to get through. We have to show the Allied forces that we are worthy of belonging to them,' they insisted to each other.

After a very brief period of recuperation, a second attack was scheduled for five days later. Although their numbers were depleted, even the cooks and drivers joined in this second onslaught. The fighting raged all night and slowly the tide began to turn in their favour.

Eventually, the shattered German troops were seen withdrawing from the abbey, frightened in case they may be isolated there. The Poles marched into the abbey, without a single shot being fired in retaliation. By ten o'clock, on the 18th May, a Polish regimental flag was flying over the highest point. They had triumphed - the Polish 2nd Corps were victors and although they didn't know it then, soon to be celebrities. A bugler began to play the Krakow Hejal – a traditional Polish military signal and Kazik and many others began to cry tears of unashamed joy.

Despite being totally weary by the intensity of the battles and mortified at the extreme loss of life, Kazik, along with the other fortunate survivors, felt exhilaration over their success. Over the coming days they considered what this victory might mean for them, could it possibly lead to a speedy return home?

Unfortunately, rather than a lull in action after the capture of Monte Cassino, General Harold Alexander, the commander of the Allied Forces, insisted they press home their advantage. The final assault commenced on the 23rd. This time, with the use of tanks, they breached the line of fortification, meaning the way was now clear for the advance towards Rome and beyond.

At last, the men were able to take a welcome break from duty. As they left the Cassino area, Kazik couldn't avoid seeing the devastation - overturned tanks, fragments of uniform and helmets everywhere and a temporary cemetery, with long columns of bodies wrapped in blankets. It was a stark reminder of the ultimate sacrifice the men had given in their support of the Allies. Kazik felt a mixture of pride at their success but great sadness at the losses. There were times during the fighting that he had come close to losing his life and he questioned how he had been fortunate enough to be spared.

Instantly, the losses brought back horrendous memories for all these former prisoners. Piles of corpses had been such a common sight in the labour camps that sadly they had almost become inured to such scenes but still it was incredibly hard to witness. The reality of war and the vast numbers of victims it claimed were all too evident.

Yet, as the troops advanced further, into the valley below, the view ahead was truly beautiful and breath-taking. The contrast was tangible. A spectacular display of red poppies and the sun's rays shining down on them, created a deep sense of peace and tranquillity.

Over the following days, the soldiers had to face a further honour – adulation from the public. Although relieved to have some free time to rest, Kazik didn't find it easy to be welcomed as a hero, everywhere his battalion ventured.

On one occasion, whilst drinking in a local tavern, some Americans insisted, 'Let us buy you all a drink.'

Kazik, unable to converse in English, hesitated.

'Polski?' they asked.

He nodded in reply.

Fortunately, one or two of the Americans had a limited knowledge of Polish.

'Come, come you are most welcome to join us,' they said, gesticulating with their arms for the men to sit down.

Then, out came a large feast, with everyone continuing to converse together, as best they could. Slowly, an awful truth began to dawn on Kazik. None of the Americans, or even the British troops had any idea of the gulag or the horrors the Polish exiles had endured. It was their understanding that the Polish soldiers had simply run away to Russia to escape the Germans.

Kazik was wary. He thought it best not to tell them too much, after all they'd been strongly advised not to speak of all they had suffered. But he was shocked- if the Americans and British soldiers had no idea of Stalin's brutal regime, then surely most of the world must be in equal ignorance. Whilst it was encouraging that these men showed great respect for all that the Poles had achieved, it was greatly discouraging to think they had no idea of the horrors they'd endured under Stalin .....would the world ever find out?

In the following weeks, news came through to the troops that the Italian authorities were authorising the building of a permanent Polish memorial, in the shadows of the abbey, in recognition of their outstanding contribution. This, they felt, was an honour indeed.

Morale was further boosted when General Leese granted that all the Polish Second Corps would now have the right to wear the British 8th Army Crusader's cross- formation badge on the right shoulder of their battle dress. In addition, General Sosnkowski, on behalf of the Polish Government in exile, awarded all the participants their first medal: the Monte Cassino Commemorative Cross. Wearing these badges of honour, filled Kazik with enormous pride and a real sense of achievement, which was certainly a very good feeling.

His work, however, was still incomplete, despite the fact that fighting in Italy had become overshadowed, with the focus of the allied offensive turning to northern Europe. Anders had some new instructions for his units, with orders that were simple and direct.

'Pursue the enemy at the highest possible speed and capture Ancona harbour.'

Throughout June, the troops fought relentlessly, despite many casualties. Finally, on the 18th July, the Germans felt they had no choice but to withdraw, allowing the port to bring in much needed supplies of fuel for the allies. Still, there was no opportunity to rest.

'We have to raise ourselves once more, for now we need to fight for control of the heavily fortified Gothic Line, running from Pisa in the west to Pesaro on the Adriatic sea,' Anders explained.

Realising his men were flagging, he did his best to encourage them, 'This is the German's last major line of defence.'

Kazik was further invigorated when he found himself promoted to second lieutenant of his artillery division.

Over the following days of August, the weather was unusually dismal but despite this, the attack began on the 19th, centring on the town of Presaro. Kazik and his fellow soldiers soon became aware that they were facing their previous fearsome adversaries – the German first parachute division. But the Polish soldiers were single minded in their determination to win.

'They are no match for us!' one of the men quipped, trying hard to remain positive.

Over the following days, the battle intensified and it seemed as if it could go either way. Finally, with great will power and strenuous effort, the 2nd Polish Corps claimed a decisive victory, after they succeeded in breaching the Gothic line. It was a great feeling but still there was no let up. In October, further orders came; they must move inland to provide support for the British 8th army, fighting further up the Adriatic coast. By the end of the month, they were advancing so rapidly and successfully that the River Senior came into view.

However, as the weather worsened, with torrential rain, the roads on which they travelled became rivers of mud. Anders had a difficult decision to make but with his usual wisdom, he explained the reasoning behind his choice.

'We are so near to achieving our target but with winter on the way, I have decided to dig in and wait for a spring offensive.'

'I guess its best we battle with the Germans rather than the weather,' one of the men retorted and others nodded in response.

By early February, the following year, after weeks of inactivity, the men were eager to resume the fight. They were especially buoyed up when news came through that the British High Command was proposing to unite the Polish 1st corps fighting in France, with the Polish 2nd Corps in Italy. Everyone felt this to be a positive move, feeling it would be advantageous to have a single Polish army, all fighting in the same theatre of war.

But what none of them realised was that a very significant meeting was taking place in Russia involving Britain, the United States and the Soviet Union. News of it slowly began to filter through the camp, over the latter days of February.

'Apparently, Winston Churchill met with Roosevelt and Stalin, at Livadia Palace near Yalta on February 4th, for a week of talks,' one of Kazik's superiors explained, 'On the agenda was the structure of post- war Europe, particularly the question of what to do about Poland and its borders.'

Keen to hear the outcome, all the men listened intently but they were certainly not expecting the bombshell that was about to be dropped on them.

'I'm sorry to tell you lads but all three men agreed that Stalin would keep his Soviet gains in Poland – all the ones that Hitler had agreed to in the Nazi/ Soviet pact of 1939.'

What! Could this devastating news really be true? The men were stunned and none more so than Kazik. He realised immediately this would include the whole of the Kresy region where his family might still be residing. Was this the absolute end to his, and all other Poles' hopes of returning to an independent and democratic Poland? In fact, he was convinced there was little chance of ever returning, for surely their land, their life style and even their families would now be lost to the Soviet Union. He felt utter despondency but stayed silent, whereas some reacted violently.

'This is an outrage! Churchill has betrayed us,' they remonstrated, 'We need to protest!'

'What can we hope to achieve?' others responded, resigned to their fate.

Tragically, a few became so demoralised they just could not accept it and over the coming days they sank into deep depression. When Kazik and his fellow Poles learnt that some of them, including thirty officers, had committed suicide, the despair within the camp escalated, with morale at an all -time low.

Unfortunately, this wasn't the last of the bad news. In July, it was reported that the Soviet authorities had established a new government in Poland known as 'The Polish Committee of National Liberation (PKWN0)' which was to be controlled from Russia and based in Lublin – the new temporary capital of Poland. Not only was it pro -Soviet, it seemed the PKWNO were now in charge of administration, even in the liberated areas of Poland.

Kazik and his fellow ex -prisoners felt immense heartbreak – they had undoubtedly lost all hope of Poland ever being independent again. 'We want a capital city liberated by Poles and not one seized by the Soviets,' was one soldier's comment and the majority agreed.

'Have all our efforts really come to this?' was the common cry.

Sadly, over the coming days, their worst fears became a reality. They were informed that even Winston Churchill, the British Prime Minister, was favouring this new Polish government and was bowing to Soviet demands; especially over the post- war Polish border demarcation. Kazik was now sure in his mind that the allies' victory, which would surely come, was obviously not going to include the liberation of his home land. This was the worst possible news. Never had he felt so demoralised and demotivated. Just what had been the point of all the suffering that he and his fellow soldiers had endured? To him this was nothing more than a complete and utter betrayal and he truly doubted if he would ever get over it. At that moment, he felt a deep sense of resentment – all those months of training and two years of fighting, with thousands of his fellow soldiers dead, now all seemingly for nothing. But there was one thing he could still have control over, one thing no-one could deny him or force him to keep quiet about. He still had a fierce sense of national pride and this strengthened his resolve to maintain his Polish identity now and forever in the future.

CHAPTER 12
FEBRUARY - 1949 SCOTLAND

Despite recovering physically from his accident, Kazik continued to struggle with his mental health. He realised financially he needed to return to work but he was feeling most unsettled. Without any prior warning, he announced to Maria that he wished to move from Hamilton.

'I think we need to find better accommodation before the baby arrives,' he explained.

'But where are you thinking of going?' Maria asked, quite perturbed at such an upheaval at this stage of her pregnancy. Besides, more pertinently, she wondered whether employment would be readily available elsewhere, although she feared to mention it.

'Why don't we have a fresh start and move away completely. I suggest we move east and look for somewhere in the capital, Edinburgh.'

Maria hesitated. 'What do you know of it?' she asked, trying hard to hide her concerns.

'It's been an important Polish centre during the war years and it's now becoming a major place for settlement by Polish army personnel, especially senior officers after their demobilisation. Our good friends- Seweryn and Elizabeth- also still live there, although I have heard they are looking to move, since he's completed his training in agriculture.'

'I hope they wouldn't move too far away,' Maria responded.

Kazik was keen to reassure her that there were other benefits.

'As well as the large Polish presence in the city, there are also a growing number of Polish institutions and centres, including a Polish Catholic Mission which might assist me in finding employment. It will also help us to maintain our Polish roots and religion. What a great bonus to bring up our child within a strong Polish community.'

Maria, eager to keep the peace and ever hopeful for a new beginning, agreed to the move. She wondered if this might be just what Kazik needed to aid his recovery, especially if he could meet and converse with more of his fellow countrymen.

Kazik immediately began to make enquiries and they soon found themselves packing up and moving to 11 Drummond Road, in the Stockbridge area of the capital. The property was located within a tenement block, containing many rooms for rent. Maria hoped her husband would be pleased to find himself living alongside many other Polish exiles.

Now, his main priority was to find employment but the move had done nothing to calm Kazik's irrational mood-swings. Maria felt herself becoming progressively anxious as he continued to act abnormally, displaying an increasing degree of aggression.

One evening, after yet another violent outburst, she realised she had put up with enough. He'd lashed out and once again grabbed her by the throat, as if attempting to suffocate her. She was terrified. This was most definitely not the Kazik she knew and loved. She recognised her husband was becoming seriously mentally ill and that he needed immediate medical attention, although he was adamant he didn't want to go into hospital.

She decided to seek help and after making enquiries, she discovered there was a Polish doctor residing down West Saville Terrace.

'I think we need to section him for a while,' the doctor suggested, after listening to what Maria had to say and observing Kazik's behaviour and responses. 'We'll send him to the Royal Edinburgh Hospital for mental disorders where he'll get the support and medication he needs.'

Maria was horrified at the thought but she knew it was the right decision. Her husband needed professional help but it left her feeling vulnerable, especially being in the early stages of pregnancy. With no family around to support her, she felt very much alone. She also realised, with her husband hospitalised, they would struggle financially so she began to consider looking for temporary work.

In desperation, she made contact with their friends Seweryn and Elizabeth, explaining Kazik's situation, pointing out all the problems it created.

Unfortunately, they had just moved on and were now living in a large Victorian mansion, known as Stroquhan House, located at Dunscore, near Dumfries in western Scotland, where they were farming. However, on hearing of her dilemma, Seweryn immediately offered his assistance.

'I'm glad to help in any way I can,' he assured her. 'For a start, I'll come over to visit Kazik. Also Elizabeth and I would like to purchase some baby clothes for the new arrival and other necessities, including a pram.'

Maria was overwhelmed by his kindness and was especially grateful for his offer of financial assistance.

Back at the hospital, Kazik was immediately assessed by two Polish psychiatrists – Dr Wikter Tomaszewskii and Dr Z Godlowski. They listened as he tried to explain his paranoia. He insisted that he was being persecuted by a gang of spies, even believing that his wife was acting as 'the chief detective'. He also felt that people around him were plotting to either murder or poison him and he recounted his visual hallucinations in which figures visited him.

Maria too was interviewed and she spoke of his escalating, violent attacks in recent weeks.

'Do you know if he has had problems in his teenage years?' they enquired.

'I don't know, I only met him within the last two years and he's never mentioned anything.'

'So, you won't know if members of his family have had any mental health issues either?'

Again Maria was unable to say but she doubted it. She recalled that Kazik had told her his father had been a Cabinet Minister so she felt it highly unlikely that he would have been capable of holding such a responsible position, if he'd suffered from similar problems.

'But I do know Kazik suffered terribly during the war and witnessed atrocities that no-one knows of…' she countered.

Then she paused – what was the point of continuing? Seeing their lack of response, she wondered whether these Polish doctors had resided in Britain for many years and had any idea of the horrors the Polish people had recently endured under Stalin. Although they listened carefully and made appropriate pleasantries, it was, she felt, mere politeness. Certainly, Maria was aware that the British people as a whole had little understanding or even knowledge of Russia's awful ongoing treatment of the Poles. But then how could they be aware when it was kept such a dark secret? She liked to believe that the British government wouldn't have supported Stalin if they had known the full extent of his brutality. However, that was not something to bring up at this time.

Over the first days of his confinement, Kazik refused food and resisted attempts to keep him in bed or make him have a bath, believing that if he was uncooperative, the doctors may discharge him. When he discovered this was not the case, he started to comply more readily. Maria saw him whenever she could but she found his behaviour very strange and disconcerting. Convinced that he had two wives who visited him on alternate days, he was sure these wives looked and talked the same, but only one was pregnant.

Seweryn also visited Kazik and felt deeply upset to find his friend so confused and troubled. He questioned what effect all those months of imprisonment might have had on him. Certainly he spoke of many prisoners of war who had suffered breakdowns and even some who had committed suicide, during or after the war.

The Scottish doctors tried to talk to Kazik but found his lack of English a great hindrance. During one consultation, he simply denied his irrational behaviour and questioned why he was in a mental hospital at all.

'Have you ever attacked your wife?' they asked.

'NO!' he replied assertively, unable to acknowledge the truth.

'What do you see as your problem?'

Kazik simply pointed to his ears, indicating they were sore. After an examination, the doctors found nothing abnormal with his ears. Was this simply an avoidance tactic to detract from his real problems? In fact, after carrying out a full medical examination, they declared that physically he was 'a strong, healthy man', except for the severe scarring on his legs. They noted that he had a good level of general intelligence and his memory was not defective although they acknowledged that he was certainly suffering from some strange delusions.

'People are trying to poison me, they want to kill me!' he insisted repeatedly.

'But why would anyone want to do that?' the doctor asked.

Kazik had no answer. He admitted he felt depressed, suicidal even and a few days into his stay, he requested a transfer to a Polish hospital where he felt he would find it easier to recover. For a while he went on hunger strike, thinking this might improve his chances. The doctors, whilst seeing through his 'tricks' as they called it, did note his continuous struggle to communicate, so they agreed on an attempt to grant him his wish. Dr Abel, his consultant, sent a letter, in mid- April, to the Ministry of Health for

Polish Services,based in London, requesting a transfer to a Polish hospital in Epsom. Sadly, to Kazik's disappointment but Maria's relief, his request was declined.

Dr Abel also sent a letter to the Regional Hospital Board, located at 6, Cambridge Street in Edinburgh asking for help and support for Maria. He addressed his appeal to Mrs Dobrzanska, who had been appointed to help Polish families in such circumstances. In reply, she explained that whilst willing to help, she would need to speak to Maria personally. Maria duly called on her and after explaining the circumstances of her pregnancy and her husband's ongoing illness, she was grateful to be given a layette for her forthcoming baby.

Throughout the following weeks, Maria focused on the future and slowly came to an important decision. She thought that maybe now was the right time to find a new home but not too far away. Kazik had become so suspicious of some of their present house mates in Drummond Street that a fresh start seemed a good idea. She decided to turn to the Polish authorities for help and was delighted when they offered her some rooms in a handsome Georgian townhouse at 14 Danube Street, which was still within the vicinity.

Over the next few months, with extensive medical help, Kazik's condition slowly improved. By early July, Dr Tomnszewaki believed he had made enough of a recovery to return to their new home for a trial period of twenty- eight days. Maria was anxious at first but as she nursed her husband with good food and gave him space to relax, she was pleased that he seemed much happier. On completion of the month, she was delighted to report back to the doctors that he had been both considerate and helpful.

On his return to the hospital, he was given a further assessment by the medical team. This time Kazik acknowledged that his suspicions against his wife and his friend had been nonsense, indicating his improved mental health. The staff were also satisfied that he seemed much more content and was displaying completely normal behaviour. There was just one other area of his life that needed addressing before his release. During the course of his final interview, the issue of employment was discussed.

'Would you like to be considered for a course at Ganton, so you can retrain?'

Kazik understood that Ganton was a rehabilitation centre but without hesitation, he declined the offer. 'I'd prefer to find employment straightaway. With my added responsibility of a new baby on the way, I need immediate work to provide me with a steady, reasonable wage.'

His employment wishes were respected and the Alien's section, in the Ministry of Labour, at Toll Cross offered him employment as a builder's labourer – a job where there was insufficient British labour available. He could start at once. After a six month's stay in hospital, Kazik finally returned home for good on the 7th of August. He seemed much happier and soon began work which was a welcome relief for both of them.

With improved health and a calmer mind, Kazik now decided to write back to the International Red Cross, giving them the go ahead to pass on his contact details to his family. Even if there was little chance of ever seeing them, he realised that he owed it to them to get in touch. Now especially seemed the optimum time; he had a settled address, he had found employment plus he was desperate for his family to know that not only was he alive but he was about to become a father.

Maria offered to visit the Post Office to buy the necessary stamps for the letter. Whilst having to queue, envelope in hand, she became deep in thought. Kazik didn't realise just how fortunate he was to still have family members, even if they did live hundreds of miles away. He should be grateful that he still had hope, if only she could have the same opportunity. However, she wouldn't consider expressing such feelings to him, for nothing would be gained by it. Instead, she simply internalised her deep sadness and yes, possibly, she had to admit, there was a slight feeling of envy too.

With the letter posted, Maria told herself to focus on the positive and remain optimistic about the future. If a reply came for Kazik, hopefully it would continue to lift his mood. But then there was the alternative possibility which had to be faced– maybe he would never hear back and that would be so hard for him. Kazik had spoken so often of his desire to go back to Poland and meet up with his family again. Hadn't that been the main reason he'd risked his life in the army so that one day his country would be liberated and he could return home? But would that day ever come?

CHAPTER 13
ITALY - 1945

Kazik and all the other exiles were feeling such a deep sense of injustice and anger, over what they saw as tantamount to a British betrayal that it was threatening to overwhelm them.

'Why the hell are we fighting now? We have no country to return to,' many cried bitterly.

Nor were they alone in their feelings. General Anders, on learning of the terms agreed by Roosevelt, Churchill, and Stalin at Yalta, immediately sat and wrote a damning letter to General Richard McCreery, leader of the British 8th Army.

'We have marched thousands of miles together and have suffered thousands of casualties. We have come from the torture of the Russian labour camps to the brink of battle which would seal our claim to be allowed to go home. Suddenly we are told, without ever being consulted, that we have no home to go to.'

Over the following days, Anders requested a face to face meeting with McCreery, determined to further convey his contempt over this decision.

'How can I ask my soldiers to go on fighting, to risk their lives for nothing? I cannot, in all conscience, demand at present any sacrifice of the soldiers' blood. I must withdraw them from the line.'

However, it wasn't long before he received a stark reply.

'If you took your troops out of the line, there would be no troops to replace them, and a ten mile gap would be opened up.'

Anders remained silent for a minute, reflecting on this simple statement, realising the true impact of the removal of his men. To be told it could ultimately prevent an Allied victory in Italy and maybe even forfeit the Polish claim to be an independent nation was definitely not what he wanted to hear.

There was only one possible response he could make.

'You can count on the Polish 2nd Corps for this coming battle. We must defeat Hitler first.'

But now Anders realised he must face his dispirited troops. Would they feel the same? Just how could he relay such news to his men, knowing they were so utterly demoralised? It would surely need all his powers of persuasion.

'We must maintain dignity and discipline worthy of the highest morale which is the attitude of every soldier of the second Polish Corps,' he told them.

The men listened- they had the highest respect for Anders but their hearts were no longer in the fight.

Over the coming days, the men found out that even the British Parliament had officially criticised Churchill for this betrayal of the Poles but sadly, it did not change anything. Britain still accepted the new Polish borders as proposed by Stalin and had even endorsed the creation of the new Polish government under Soviet control.

Churchill tried to make amends with a radio broadcast, telling the Poles that after the war, England would welcome them with employment and homes. But for many, including Kazik, this wasn't welcome news at all.

However, when fighting was resumed in the spring, they tried to adopt a new attitude. They might have lost their country but they were determined to keep their honour. On the ninth of April, they began their final offensive. Their resolve proved invaluable as their attack was so successful, the German parachute division soon disintegrated. Within six days, they had captured Imola and after a further six days, they were able to liberate the city of Bologna. The men quickly captured the 1st Parachute Division's battle flag and presented it to General Anders as a trophy.

The inhabitants of Bologna were overjoyed, immediately treating the Poles as heroes. The troops were equally pleased when they not only received a letter of thanks from the mayor, Joseph Dozza but were also honored with a congratulatory letter from McCreery:

'You have shown a splendid fighting spirit, endurance and skill in this great battle. I send my warmest congratulations and admiration to all ranks.'

Even the British Foreign Secretary, Harold Macmillan, publically acknowledged the Polish 2nd Corps' success. In an open letter he wrote, 'I have underestimated the marvellous dignity and devotion of Anders and his comrades. They fought with distinction in the front of attack in the last battles of April. They had lost their country but they kept their honour.'

Despite this adulation, the men still held a deep underlying resentment. The atmosphere in their camp became increasingly fraught, as the reality of their situation hit home.

'We have been treated more than unjustly,' they ranted, 'Think of all the men who have given their lives in this war and for what?'

The liberation of Bologna may have ended fourteen months of operation in the Italian campaign, but the Polish 2nd Corps had lost over eleven thousand men during that time yet what had they gained? It seemed Poland, although free of German occupation, was now, with the consent of its western allies, under the yoke of Russian communism.

Therefore when news came through, in early May, that Hitler was dead after committing suicide and that Germany had finally surrendered, there was no great celebration amongst the troops.

'For us, it is a defeat in victory,' was a frequent grievance heard in the camp, knowing the war had resolved nothing and they faced an uncertain future.

'Why don't we form our own army and drive up north and liberate Poland ourselves?' suggested some of the more optimistic soldiers.

'Do we stand any chance of success?' asked others.

In the end, most agreed it was an impossible task.

The men, utterly discouraged, were very subdued as they celebrated the Polish Armed Forces Day for the last time on the 15th of August. They joined a huge parade, held on the airfield at Loretta, attended by dignitaries including General Anders and the departing commander in chief, Field Marshall Harold Alexander.

Within two weeks, World War Two was officially declared to be over but now the Allies were faced with a real issue. What was to be done with all these Polish exiles of the Second Corps, if they couldn't or didn't want to return home to a land which was no longer theirs?

General Anders was summoned to London for talks with the British Foreign Secretary, Ernest Bevin. Bevin suggested that the men should be demobilised and repatriated to Poland, having reached an agreement with the TKJN, on the terms of this repatriation. Speaking in the House of Commons, he promised to send a document outlining these terms to every member of the Polish Second Corps.

Kazik, along with his fellow soldiers, received the document, translated into poor Polish, with bewilderment. The majority of the 112,000 soldiers in the Corps felt disconsolate on two levels. They had not been expecting demobilisation just yet but more significantly, why would they want to return to Poland when their homes were now part of the Soviet Union?

Then suddenly, it seemed there was a change of plan – the idea of sending them 'home' had apparently been abandoned in favour of transferring them to Britain for demobilisation. It seemed Britain had decided to offer them sanctuary, announcing the establishment of a 'Polish Resettlement Corps' which would provide support and accommodation until they were able to find work and housing.

Kazik wasn't sure how he felt about living in England but did he have an alternative? He was considering his options when a further British announcement brought news which stunned him.

Tuesday, the 8th of May, 1946 was designated as Victory in Europe Day, with a triumphal victory parade planned for all the allied armed forces in Central London. Yet it seemed, unbelievably, the Poles weren't going to be invited. As the Labour government, under Clement Attlee, was keen not to offend Stalin, they'd decided, it would be best to bar the hundreds of thousands of Poles, who had fought under British command, from attending. Remarkably, however, he was willing to allow the Red Army and communist Poland to participate. What irony!

Kazik, along with all his fellow Poles, felt total, utter rejection and disbelief. How could the Allies be so cruel to a Polish army who had not only been the fourth largest combatant force fighting the Germans but had undoubtedly assisted in their defeat and served so valiantly? Where was British loyalty? Why had their heroic war efforts not even been acknowledged, let alone rewarded? It was injustice on a huge scale although, apparently, there was nothing they could do about it.

News came through that a contingent of Polish airmen did receive an invitation, as the RAF had insisted on it, but they chose to decline, as a protest at the exclusion of all their army and navy compatriots. But still it made no difference.

In the days that followed, Kazik's mind was awash with doubts and misgivings. Did he really want to settle in England, feeling as he did about Churchill's betrayal? Also he had to consider his inability to speak the language for he certainly wasn't in any mood to try to learn it. He was further troubled by the question of employment. What work opportunities would be available for him and how would he survive and not just financially? Although much stronger physically in recent months, the last few years had been punishing mentally and he was aware that he was not really coping. He was sure too that many others felt equally perturbed.

In fact, when General Anders gave instructions that they were to meet near Ancona on 15th June for their last day, the tension in the air was palpable. All the soldiers stood side by side in a hushed and respectful mood, recognising the solemnity of the event. Each unit was read a very poignant but hugely significant vow. A vow signed by General Anders himself: **To continue the struggle for the liberty of Poland, however difficult that might prove to be.**

Kazik felt overwhelmed but he displayed no emotion outwardly. He had learnt to repress his anger during those long months of imprisonment, choosing as always to internalise it.

With a crushing sadness, the men from all the units in the north watched as their equipment, vehicles and armour were all taken to a depot south of Milan where they too were crushed and reduced to scrap. Many of the soldiers began to weep as they saw their past and undoubtedly their future, wiped away in this symbolic act.

After being taken to nearby railway stations, they began their journey to Naples for their transportation to the United Kingdom.

The War Office had drawn up plans to disperse the one hundred and twelve thousand men throughout Britain. Most now fully understood that returning to Poland was not an option, knowing this new communist regime would consider them to be 'enemies of the state.' The very fact that they'd fought in the Polish 2nd Corps meant they had shown loyalty to the Polish government in exile and disloyalty to the Soviets. Consequently, a return to their homeland could pose a real threat - with the distinct possibility of transportation to Siberia or even worse….

The men boarded the ship, bound for Liverpool; a journey that they were told would take a week. It was an opportunity to relax but many became plagued by the usual sea sickness.

Already feeling apprehensive –unsure of what reception they would be given by the English – a stark warning was to come.

On their arrival on British soil, their commanding officer ordered:

'DO NOT SPEAK ABOUT YOUR TIME IN THE SOVIET UNION.'

Kazik realised this command came down from the British Government, who were in fear of angering Moscow and did not want the 'good' name of Stalin to be besmirched. Despite its injustice, Kazik took the warning to heart, realising there was little to be gained from dwelling on his ordeals. He had pondered over the events of the past five years, since his capture in 1941, so many times. So many haunting memories were hidden within his mind, so much evil he had witnessed with human depravity at its worst. Perhaps it would be best if he tried to forget his past and not speak of it to anyone ....ever.

Perhaps too, it would be best if he accepted this new chance of life in Britain, especially since Stalin had recently revoked their Polish citizenship, insisting that if any members of the Polish army tried to return to Poland in the future, they would be refused entry.

But he recognised this decision was fraught with problems. Within a few days of being issued with his army exit medical, an alien identity certificate and a national registration identity card, ready for his transfer from a military to a civilian life, he felt most uncomfortable. Did he really want to be a British citizen? Could he accept their culture when his own meant so much to him? Besides, would they ever accept him?

He was certainly adamant about one issue - he didn't want to be classified as a British subject, neither at that point in time nor in the future. He was so proud to be Polish. No-one could take that away from him and he intended to be loyal to his Polish roots for the rest of his life.

CHAPTER 14
EDINBURGH - 1949

Kazik had not long been out of hospital when on Sunday 21st August, 1949, Maria was taken to Western General Hospital in Edinburgh and gave birth to a baby girl at 2.25pm in the afternoon.

'Let's call her Olenka, (Polish for Aleksandra) Kazik suggested, as he saw his daughter for the first time.

'That's just perfect for my beautiful corka, my little zabka (froglet),' replied Maria, using typical Polish endearments for her.

It moved Maria to see Kazik's tears of joy as he hugged his precious daughter. She could see how proud he was of this beautiful baby and that was a good feeling.

'She has your intense blue eyes and just a hint of your black wavy hair,' he said smiling, as he gently stroked her face.

'Yes and she has your strong lungs!' Maria replied when Olenka suddenly let out a wail.

They laughed and Maria was heartened. Maybe the birth of their child might lift Kazik's spirits and help him put aside some of his deep anguish. Hopefully the bad days were behind them and they could start to enjoy being a new family.

Over the coming days, Kazik continued to be an attentive father and enjoyed cradling the baby on his return from work.

'It's important we speak to her in Polish, Maria,' he insisted, as he chatted away to Olenka in his thick Polish accent. 'I want to raise her so that she knows all about her Polish ancestors and learns their traditions and can speak their language,' he explained, 'I am absolutely determined that she grows up to be genuinely Polish rather than be known as a British subject of Polish descent.'

Maria willingly accepted these demands, knowing how important they were to her husband. Besides, she realised Kazik's command of English was so limited, he wouldn't be able to chat to the baby in any language other than his own. But she kept such a thought to herself. She was just grateful that her husband appeared to be happy. Certainly he seemed to be more settled and positive since Olenka's arrival and the disturbed and violent behaviour he'd displayed previously had now diminished.

In order to comply with these wishes, whenever Olenka needed soothing, Maria serenaded her with Polish songs, ones that she remembered from her own childhood. She made sure that she only read stories from Polish books, obtained from the local library. She also agreed to follow Kazik's wish to have a Catholic baptism for their daughter.

'Let's invite Seweryn to be her godfather,' Kazik suggested and Maria thought this a good idea.

Seweryn was more than happy to accept their invitation. He and his wife attended the christening and once again they were generous with their gifts.

Each day that followed, on his return from his shift, Kazik spent time with his daughter, whispering to her in his native tongue and making promises.

'If only my family could meet you….. one day, one day, I **will** take you to my homeland and you **will** learn what it means to be Polish.'

'Maybe that will happen sooner than you think,' Maria replied unexpectedly one evening.

Kazik looked up, his face puzzled as his wife held aloft an envelope.

'This came in the post this morning,' she said, barely able to hide her excitement.

She handed it over and watched eagerly to gauge Kazik's reaction, as first he studied the Polish handwriting on the envelope and then fumbled to open it. He immediately turned the letter over to reveal the writer and let out a gasp.

'It's from my sister, Eugenia!'

For a while the room fell silent as he took in the contents. His pained face contorted at times whilst at others, he smiled and nodded in approval.

'This is wonderful news. My sisters, they both survived.. and so has Janek,' Kazik repeated, trying to take it all in. 'Here Maria read it for yourself, there's too much to tell you.'

For the rest of that evening, in between feeding and rocking Olenka, they both spent the time discussing his family's news. Much of it had been so hard to read ……

Belorussia 1949

Dear Kazik,

It was a truly wonderful day when we heard from the Red Cross that they had made contact with you. We'd been desperate for so long to hear from you and had even begun to assume you hadn't survived the war.

We wonder how you endured your imprisonment at Stara Vileyka . Certainly your sister Werca and I found our time there incredibly hard, little realising that worse was to come for us. We were transported from there into the depths of Siberia. It was absolutely dreadful – such a remote wilderness area with conditions that were extremely harsh and unrelenting. The winter was bitter, with temperatures dropping as low as minus fifty and I remember the ground being almost permanently covered with frost and even the rivers became frozen. Our surroundings were largely uninhabited, except for a wide variety of wild life. We knew only the toughest could survive in such conditions and we were convinced, it was the beginning of the end for us.

We were allocated primitive wooden huts where we slept or rather tried to. They were always heavily guarded yet such tight security seemed pointless, I doubted if anyone would ever be able to escape. Even for the few that did, I'm sure they wouldn't have survived for long out in that frozen wasteland.

So often we looked out for you Kazik, amongst the vast number of prisoners in the camp, some of them even came from Russia but many more were Poles. Most of the men were set to work in the lucrative gold mines – all rewards going to Josef Stalin no doubt.

Werca and I were devastated when we were separated soon after our arrival. It turned out that I was the more fortunate because as soon as the guards realised I was a talented seamstress, they assigned me to one of the many textile factories making clothes. Although the work rate was relentless and the job tedious, I was lucky not having to endure the harsh outdoor conditions. Whereas poor Werca, she was set to work in the fields, on one of the many farms. She had to endure hard physical labour, coping with the sub -zero temperatures in the winter and then be plagued by thousands of insects in the brief summer months. They caused her immense discomfort and she was fully aware they carried disease and lived in fear of it.

Every day we faced a constant absence of palatable food and a lack of drinking water. It was unbearable and affected us all physically – we watched as many of our fellow prisoners succumbed to starvation and so many died as a result. Werca has told me she survived on what she considered 'gifts of nature' – food such as nuts and berries that grew in the fields, giving her some extra nourishment.

Life for her had been so unbearable, she still refuses to speak of it and is adamant that it will stay that way in the future. It has left her with an embarrassing physical problem too that she still has no idea how to deal with, despite the passing of the years.

When our release came, we were taken to a displacement camp where we had a long period of recuperation. I think we were among the more fortunate, as our incarceration was much shorter than many ….which meant we survived. We witnessed some terrible suffering but it is in the past now…

We had absolutely nothing in the way of documentation on our release but we were given a mountain of paper work to complete. I decided this was an ideal opportunity for me to start life again and that a reduction in my age might be advantageous. So I wrote on the forms that I was born in 1918, which is actually when my younger sister Maria was born.

When we returned to Zupran, we were keen to catch up with so many of the opportunities we had missed, including meeting up with eligible young men. One day, Werca and I met two brothers – Janek and Jusef- it quickly led to us both planning a wedding.

Speaking of Janek, I'm sure you are keen to hear of your much loved younger brother. Well he survived the war, but only just. He fulfilled his youthful dream of joining the Polish army under General Sikorski, serving in Pozan but unfortunately he caught the dreaded typhus. He too was one of the lucky ones who survived but after his recovery, he left the army and started work in the building trade. Janek's married now to Janina – a girl from Wasilkow – and he's a father too – he has a young son - Wiesiek.

I'm sure you remember how resourceful he's always been, making himself an income right from a young age when he went to collect mushrooms and logs from the forest to sell. Well, today he enjoys breeding coypu in his back yard –he uses their skins to make luxurious coats, which are proving to be a really good earner.

Ever since that day when you were arrested, Janek has been desperate to trace you – as indeed we all have. When we hadn't heard from you for so long, we'd almost given up hope, thinking you must be one of those thousands of unfortunate ones whose life had been snuffed out.

But then, I'd had an idea. I'd heard the International Red Cross had a tracing service and I wondered if they might be able to locate you or at least tell us what had happened to you. We knew it was a big ask but what had we to lose? We are now so happy that we contacted them.

But now I have some less happy news to tell you. We no longer live in Zupran. The Russians virtually forced us to move out. In 1945, they extended their borders westwards into our area of Poland. They gave us an ultimatum -either we become sovietised or we move further west to the Polish territories agreed at Yalta. For me it was an easy decision, I emigrated to Zielona Gora, which was actually part of Germany before the war. But your sister, twenty- seven year old Maria, decided not to move. She was happy to conform to the Soviet Union's views and live under their culture. It was hard for us to come to terms with her decision but she seemed happy, so in the end we accepted her choice. I'm sure she believed that one day the situation would be reversed and that the Russians would lose their dominance.

I'm also sorry to tell you that we have lost our dear babunia. She grew so weary with everything that went on. … I won't go into detail as I don't wish to upset you.

Instead, I want you to know how overjoyed we are, especially to learn you are married and expecting your first child.

What a wonderful day it would be if ever we were to meet up again….. though we daren't hope.

Please write back and update us with your news.

Your loving sister,Eugenia.

CHAPTER 15
EDINBURGH TO MANCHESTER - 1949 - 1958

'To think they had given me up for dead. They must have been so happy to hear from me,' Kazik mused after reading Eugenia's letter yet again.

'And delighted to know you were going to be a father,' Maria remarked, 'in fact we must write back immediately and tell them Olenka has arrived.'

Kazik agreed and it brought him great comfort, knowing he was back in touch with his family.

'We shall have some more news to tell them very soon,' Maria quietly announced, a few days later.

Just four months after Olenka's arrival, Maria had recognised the signs and realised she was expecting another baby.

Kazik seemed pleased to learn he was to be a father again although Maria hoped the extra responsibility wouldn't unsettle him. It would be hard to have two children so close together and costly too- especially if it was a boy this time.

Maria pondered over the problem and ever resourceful, she made up her mind to ask for more help from the Polish club. Providing for Olenka's need was already an ongoing drain on their limited finances. She sent a letter outlining her concerns and was delighted to receive a prompt reply. If she was prepared to call round to their office, they would be willing to offer support once more. Maria was soon collecting numerous baby items which she really appreciated.

But this was not a permanent solution to their lack of funds. Kazik, Maria decided, needed a better job than merely working in a factory. She was keen to return to work too but realised, without child care, it was a non-starter. Being at home all day, made her feel rather lonely, how she wished she knew more people in Edinburgh, especially someone who may be able to child mind. Slowly the beginnings of an idea formed in her mind which she mulled over for several weeks.

One evening, she tentatively broached the subject with Kazik.

'I'd really like to return to the Manchester area, after all we know several Polish families who live there. It would be good to see the Novaks and their two young children again, especially now we have a family ourselves.

'Yes, I'm willing to consider that,' Kazik responded, to Maria's surprise. 'After the baby's arrived, I'll look to see if there are any jobs available, maybe in a colliery down in that area,' he promised.

Relieved, Maria concentrated on preparing for her forthcoming confinement and on Saturday, the last day of September in 1950, she went into hospital. Both of them were truly delighted when she safely gave birth to a son and a baby brother for her little 'froglet'. He was such a bonny baby with his mother's dark hair although she insisted he had the look of his father.

'He's going to be tall like you,' Maria quipped on seeing the length of his legs.

Over the next few days, they settled on a name which meant something to them both.

'Let's call him Seweryn,' Kazik suggested and Maria agreed, equally keen to acknowledge the support their friend had given them and it seemed such an appropriate way of expressing their gratitude.

'How about Seweryn Daniel?' she added and Kazik immediately expressed his approval.

Due to the hard work and busyness of their lives, the move back to Manchester was delayed until late 1952. Kazik managed to secure employment at Agecroft Colliery in Pendlebury, as a maintenance engineer, plus they located a flat to rent in the Moss-side area of south Manchester.

'It's rather small but it'll do for now,' Marie remarked when she first saw the two simple rooms with just an outside toilet and a cement backyard.

'This will only be temporary,' Kazik assured her, 'we'll put our name down for a council house in Manchester.'

He was happy to live in Moss-side as it had a strong Polish community, with many Polish organisations. This included the biggest ex-serviceman's club in Britain, known as Dom Combatants, in Shrewsbury Street. Not only was it a social centre, it also provided a place where you could seek legal advice, learn of job opportunities, as well as offering counselling and support. There were also Polish doctors, dentists and shops which were a great attraction for Kazik when he was so desperate to maintain his Polish heritage.

Kazik, as expected, found his new job involved shift work ; either from six in the morning until two in the afternoon, two to ten in the evening or all night but he had never shirked hard graft. Being a resourceful and proud man, he was simply grateful to be earning a good wage.

Meanwhile, Maria's life was over taken with caring for her two toddlers but she was constantly troubled with painful tooth ache. A visit to the local dentist confirmed what she feared.

'You need to have all your teeth removed,' he informed her.

She wasn't too keen to undergo the procedure but knew it had to be done. Afterwards, with a full set of false teeth, she accepted that adaptions would have to be made but she took such problems in her stride. She had learnt not to worry over such trifles. Life was more important than coping with dentures. She fully understood why her teeth had become so loose. She was aware that teeth needed calcium to remain strong but during her developing years, her restrictive diet had been sadly lacking in such minerals. But she didn't speak of the reason behind it to the dentist or even to Kazik.

She still remembered being told not to speak of anything regarding her past - besides she had tried to wipe such memories from her mind... they were just too awful. She doubted if she would ever tell anyone of her appalling ordeal.

On the whole though, Maria began to recognise that life really seemed to be improving.

'We've been offered a council house,' Kazik informed her early in 1953. Its address is 105, Finningley Road which is in the Blackley area of Manchester, where I'm told there's a brand new housing estate.'

Maria was thrilled to hear this and was especially pleased when she saw the three bed-roomed houses for the first time. It was in a pleasant residential area and was the last house in a row of terraced dwellings. There was a steep garden area to the front, with five steps up to the front door. Behind the house was a small rear garden with an outside brick shed whilst to the side was a snicket. This led to a large area of grassland, which climbed into a steep hill, plus a small pathway leading to the main road and several shops.

'Having a garden is such a treat and that grassland will be ideal for the children to play on when they're a bit bigger, as it's away from the traffic. Plus it's good to have some shops within walking distance,' Maria commented.

'And I'll be able to cycle to work from here,' her husband replied, ever keen to save money, although the colliery was over five miles away.

It seemed there were several other young families in the street and over the coming weeks, Kazik and Maria made friends with George and Edna Hawk, an English couple who lived at the other end of the road. They too had a girl and a boy, Brenda and Robert, of similar age to Olenka and Seweryn which gave them a common bond. Mrs Hawk always managed to draw a smile out of Kazik, as being unable to pronounce his name, she kept referring to him as Charles. Kazik, in turn, really took to their children and especially loved to tease Brenda. In time, they arranged social outings together on their days off and the children loved visiting the local Heaton Park or wandering up to Heaton Mills where there was a large reservoir by the River Irk.

However, despite socialising with this English couple, Kazik continued with his determination not to become remotely westernised. When anyone ever asked, he always insisted they were a Polish family and not an English one. Adhering to this belief, he still resolutely refused to speak to the children in any language other than Polish. The children accepted it, not knowing any differently whereas their mother always chatted to them in English. Yet she too reverted to Polish when conversing with her husband.

He was equally determined, over the following months and years, to maintain his Catholic roots, expecting all religious festivals to be celebrated in traditional Polish ways. Sundays were dominated by his attendance at mass, although Maria didn't go with him. During Lent, he ensured no meat was eaten and on days such as Good Friday, he expected the family to respect it as a Holy day. One particular Good Friday, his wife hung the washing out to dry in the back garden.

'Fetch it back in Maria!' Kazik ordered the moment he spotted it.

Easter Sunday became a favourite family occasion with a special feast which included the Polish tradition of eating both hard boiled eggs, painted with brightly coloured dye and special wafers, with religious symbols, in remembrance of Christ's passion.

Every week, Kazik made a point of visiting his local library to borrow Polish books, historical ones becoming his particular favourite. Each day he called at a local shop, knowing it sold a Polish newspaper, always eager to keep himself abreast of political events in Europe, especially those involving his homeland.

He followed, with ever increasing anger and frustration, as Stalin installed communist governments in most of Eastern Europe, forming an eastern bloc, separated from the west by what Churchill referred to as 'The Iron Curtain'. Its headquarters were in Warsaw and they sought to obtain totalitarian control over each of these countries, including his beloved Poland. Kazik felt his homeland was completely 'disappearing' and he keenly felt the injustice of being unable to go back home. Hadn't he fought and helped the Russians in their fight against the Germans? How Stalin had betrayed him.

Then one evening in March 1953, on returning from work, Kazik went to sit and read his paper and was stunned by the headline that faced him.

'Maria, Maria, Stalin has died!' he shouted over to her, as she prepared tea in the kitchen.

'Has he been killed or was it natural causes?' Maria asked.

'Some seem to be suggesting he's been poisoned but most attribute his demise to a stroke,' Kazik replied, 'I don't particularly care, all that concerns me is how it might affect our future.'

Maria smiled in response; she knew how much her husband had hated Stalin and how keen he was to see change.

Over the next few weeks, the newspaper reported that Stalin's successors had begun to dismantle some of the labour camps. Then even more welcome news came through of an amnesty, granted to all non -political prisoners plus all political prisoners sentenced to less than five years.

Kazik now began to wonder if returning to his homeland might become a real possibility. Would it be a good time to consider visiting his family … he must make some enquiries? But first, Maria reminded him, he must let his brother and sisters know he'd moved back to England.

There was also another pressing matter that needed to be discussed. Olenka and Seweryn were approaching school age which meant a decision was required over their choice of school.

'I'm keen to send them to a private school,' Kazik suggested and Maria happily agreed, for when it came to the question of education, both wanted the children to receive the best they could afford. Maria had managed to find herself a temporary job to supplement their income but they both understood that sacrifices would have to be made, making any thought of a holiday out of the question. Neither of them particularly minded staying in their present council house, nor did it concern them that the décor and furniture were basic and their possessions few, for they agreed that every penny earned should be carefully spent, rather than wasted on any of life's extravagances. To them luxuries were just that and not the key issue; the important thing was that the children gained opportunities to be successful so that ultimately they would make their parents proud.

After consideration, they chose the local Roman Catholic school, St Joseph's, which both children started when just five. Olenka found it quite hard to settle, feeling isolated and somewhat lonely whereas Seweryn adapted to its strict regime much more easily.

Not only did Kazik want to see his children achieve success educationally, in their spare time he also insisted they learn to play the piano. Every week, brother and sister went for their lessons and once again Danny showed great promise. These pursuits placed added demands on their finances, so Kazik always ensured he kept tight rein on their spending.

Maria decided, now the children were at school, she would like to better herself and find alternative employment to her present low paid, unskilled manual work. She was much more outgoing than her husband and was keen to make use of her great intelligence. The idea of becoming a nurse appealed to her, so she undertook several months of hard training.

She was delighted that her mentors were suitably impressed with her commitment and ability but one thing held her back - her limited command of written English. After making the acquaintance of a Polish consultant, he arranged for her to take the necessary exams in Polish. With this hindrance removed, she was now able to achieve great success, passing all her exams to qualify as a state registered nurse.

For Maria this new title gave her a real sense of achievement and satisfaction and she soon found employment at Crumpsall Hospital, in the northern part of the city. She loved caring for the patients and felt fulfilled in her role. She hoped Kazik was proud of her success even if he never said so.

However, she certainly knew of her husband's pride when news came from St Joseph's that Seweryn had won a scholarship to the prestigious Xaverian College in Lower Park Road,

Manchester which he would attend as soon as he was seven. This grammar school, founded in 1862 by Roman Catholic brothers, was principally for boys of that faith and had the motto: 'In harmony, small things grow.' Although Kazik didn't verbalise his thoughts, Maria knew this honour meant such a lot to him and that he would encourage his son to give his absolute best effort to his studies.

For the whole family, it seemed life was definitely improving but always in the back of Maria's mind were nagging doubts whether this period of stability would last…..

1956

'Your husband's had an accident,' the man standing at the door informed Maria, 'he's been taken to hospital.'

Maria's mind began to race, thinking back to the day when he'd burnt himself and wondering just what might have happened this time.

'Don't worry,' the man reassured her, 'he's not badly hurt, he's fallen down at the pit and we think he's broken his collar bone.'

Maria was relieved it was nothing serious but she was still fearful, hoping the stress of it wouldn't trigger one of his 'moods'. She remembered only too well that his last accident had marked the start of his mental breakdown. Hopefully, this minor one would not be a catalyst for a reoccurrence of his 'paraphrenia' as the doctors had called it.

She had every reason to be concerned. Although he recovered quickly from his physical injuries, the doctor ordered him to take time off work for a while. Over the next month, he simply stayed in the house, spending most of the day sitting and staring vacantly into the fire or worse still, pacing the floor.

Olenka saw this as a great opportunity – it wasn't often she saw her father, due to his shift patterns- but now he was around when she returned home from school. She tried to chat with him, desperately wanting him to play but he didn't appear to listen to anything she said.

'Leave your father alone, let him be,' her mother advised but it upset Olenka to see him so sad.

With his enforced rest, the added financial worry created by his lack of earnings, caused further deterioration in his mood and gradually family life began to disintegrate. Maria did her best to protect the children from the truth regarding their father's condition but it was difficult to conceal.

112

Kazik usually prepared the evening meal for the family, whenever Maria was nursing, in fact he relished making his favourite Polish recipes, including potato cake with sour cream or baking apples in the fire. But now he seemed to have retreated into his own world and showed no interest in cooking or indeed in anything.

The local nuns, when aware of their difficult home situation, decided to intervene by offering Maria a break. They agreed to send Olenka and Seweryn to two private boarding schools for a while; Olenka to Bognor Regis in West Sussex and Seweryn to Broadstairs in Kent. The children had mixed feelings, excited to be having 'a holiday' but sad to be going away without 'mum' and 'dad'.

On their departure, Maria handed them both a brown paper bag, hoping to ease their goodbyes.

'Open this later,' she whispered, 'I think you'll like what's inside.'

Once on the train, Olenka had a peep inside and realised her mother had given her quite a rare treat. It was a large bar of chocolate which she decided to save for later. Clinging on to it throughout the journey, she was mortified on her arrival at her new temporary home, to have everything taken from her, including the brown bag. She never did get to eat the chocolate.

Despite her young age, Olenka settled quickly and became quite contented. The school was near the coast and she enjoyed playing on the beach with new young friends, who took to calling her Sandra. This really pleased her, having an English name made her feel so much more accepted. Perhaps, she considered, she should revert to this name in future but then she realised there was one huge drawback – her father would certainly be very disapproving.

On speaking to her brother later she discovered he was also coming round to the idea of calling himself Danny but he too had his reservations, due to his father's likely reaction. They were both fully aware of how much he wanted them to remain Polish.

After several long weeks, 'Sandra' and 'Danny' returned home but it was 'Olenka' and 'Seweryn' who were reunited with their mother and father. After a period of rest and medication at Salford Hospital, their father had recovered enough to return home and had now resumed his daily shift at the colliery. He made no mention of their enforced 'holiday' and they soon concluded it was best not to tell him of their preferred name choice. Undoubtedly, he would always call them by their Polish names but from now on, when out of his company, they became known as Sandra and Danny.

Kazik and Maria resumed their weekly visits to the Polish club where they regularly met with their old friends, the Novaks. Julian was always willing to listen as Kazik reminisced about their mutual homeland and they frequently discussed their future options regarding a return. However, Kazik made no mention of his recent struggle with his mental health.

Maria also found comfort in her friendship with Halina. The two of them could laugh together over irrelevancies, even joking about the local 'peasants', although when it came to personal problems, just like her husband, Maria was not so willing to share them with her friend …

In truth, Maria was becoming quite worried for she had several issues that were troubling her but they remained silent fears. Her recent concerns over Kazik's mental status had made her question her marriage once again; she had to admit that there were times when she was frightened of him. She realised too, the children were growing up, becoming ever more aware of their father's disturbed behaviour but she was eager to protect them from the full reality of his illness. What choice did she have? She didn't want to leave him but neither did she want the children to suffer.

She also had her own personal worries, particularly over her health – she had recently made a rather perturbing discovery… but she held such concerns close, deciding not to share them with anyone for the time being. For in the past she had experienced far worse and had learnt to cope on her own.

She had never spoken or confided in anyone about what had happened when she was a teenager, living in Warsaw with her parents. Back then, she had had to deal with trauma on an unimaginable scale. …

CHAPTER 16
AUTUMN 1941 -1943
WARSAW - WESTERN POLAND

Whilst the German onslaught was taking place in Russia, with troops advancing on Moscow in October 1941, horrific events were also happening in Western Poland.

The capital city, Warsaw, had surrendered to Nazi Germany back in 1939 when the Germans had declared the western portion of Poland to be a part of greater Germany. Now, Warsaw was ruled from the city of Krakow by Hans Frank.

It had long been a cosmopolitan city, with a large number of Jewish citizens. But to the Nazis, the Jews were seen as enemies and therefore they'd been rounded up and segregated by the Germans in October 1940 and forced to live in a ghetto, in the heart of the city. Although they numbered in excess of four hundred thousand, they now existed in an area of just one square mile.

The non-Jewish inhabitants were residing in what was known as the Aryan side of the city and they were threatened with death if they sought to help any Jews escape out of the ghetto.

During this time, Maria was living in the Aryan side of the city, with her well–to-do parents, Dr and Mrs Poleszczuk. Her father, born in 1901, was a respected doctor and both he and his wife, were highly educated. Maria, born on 21st September 1927, was an only child and was doted on by Francis and Maria. She was clever and capable and doing well at school, displaying a particular love of languages and an unusual interest in politics. She also enjoyed dancing and would practise her skills at the local theatre.

As she grew into an attractive teenager, the lives of all the citizens were becoming increasingly bleak. The residents regularly witnessed acts of atrocity against the Jewish community, particularly in 1942 when they experienced what was dubbed 'the final solution.' Hundreds of them were removed from the ghetto by the Nazis and Maria understood that they'd been taken to a death camp for extermination in the gas chambers. That thought was too unbearable for her as a young, sensitive girl and she lived in fear of what the Nazis might eventually do to her own family.

In recent months, bombs had been dropped on complete blocks of houses, killing innocent women and children indiscriminately. Tanks had rolled into the outskirts of the city, intent on using their heavy artillery to destroy hospitals, churches, historic buildings, in fact all of the city's national treasures.

The Nazi's ultimate aim was to completely subdue the residents of Warsaw. But some Polish inhabitants were showing great resilience, with a determination to fight back.

Every evening, throughout the following days and weeks, Maria and her mother were fearful. Would their father return home safely after work? Would their home be the next target for attack? Would their lives ever return to normal? They doubted it, as they witnessed events worsening on a daily basis. By the autumn of 1942, horrific statistics were being banded around. There was talk that in excess of sixty thousand inhabitants had lost their lives.

For the remainder of the year, the Nazis consolidated their take-over of the city. Maria and her parents watched, in utter hopelessness, as their good standard of living continued to drop, especially with the introduction of rationing, due to severe food shortages.

It was now apparent that the Germans were intent on expelling the entire civilian population of Warsaw, not just the Jewish community. Every one of the remaining inhabitants felt a deep sense of terror. When they went to bed in the evening, they had no idea if they would be woken and arrested before morning came. In the day time, innocent passers-by would be taken off the street and publically executed.

'I'm frightened,' Maria's mother confided to her husband, time and time again, 'What will become of us? Should we leave or have we left it too late?'

Francis had no idea how to calm his wife.

'They still seem to be focusing on the few remaining Jews,' he told her with a degree of reassurance, although it saddened his heart to witness their suffering, knowing they were totally innocent of any crime.

Certainly in previous months, he'd been approached by various gangs of Jewish children, begging for food and money. Undoubtedly, they'd been sent by their parents, trapped inside the ghetto, presumably hoping their children's innocence might arouse sympathy and illicit help. For Francis, particularly as a doctor, it had been heart breaking to see how undernourished and ragged these youngsters had become but he was fully aware that any kind of response to their pleas would have been unwise. Immediate reprisal would have come from one of the many guards parading the streets.

'The street is a frightening place to be,' Francis remarked, understanding his wife's trepidation, 'so maybe you should avoid going out, unless it is really necessary.'

Then turning to his daughter, he was keen to remind her, 'When you do venture out, you must remember to step aside onto the street, if you pass a German guard. '

'What if I forget?' Maria asked innocently.

'You MUSN'T forget,' her father replied quite forcibly.

'Why, they wouldn't hurt me as an Aryan, would they?' Maria persisted.

Francis paused, reluctant to answer.

'Tell me father, what would they do?' Maria repeated.

'If you forget …you will end up with a bullet in your head!'

The words were chilling and Maria flinched.

'Well, I just wish you didn't have to go out to work, please be careful,' she responded, giving her father a hug.

Francis hadn't wanted to scare his daughter but he'd recently heard stories that had truly alarmed him, not that he would ever share them with his wife, let alone his daughter. It was said that the Nazis were rounding up teenage girls and young women to work as sex slaves in military brothels. He'd heard of one soldier opening a girl's coat to grope her, remarking, 'This one is ideal for bed.' He also knew that the Germans had begun to specifically target people like himself; those who had any political or cultural status such as civil servants, clergymen and landowners, rounding them up for execution.

'I promise to be careful,' he replied, 'and I suggest from now on, I accompany you to school every day.'

Maria and her mother nodded in approval but they all felt incredibly anxious.

Over the following days and weeks, Maria's mother fretted constantly and jumped at the slightest of sounds outside, especially as darkness fell – any footsteps in the passage way or the sound of hushed voices made her fearful.

Once or twice, they heard more pleasant sounds of music. A few remaining Jewish musicians were trying to earn money to help their desperate families. Maria would respond by throwing the odd coin out of the window but again she feared reprisal. Sometimes, they heard the terrifying sound of a gunshot, immediately followed by a deafening silence. It was heart breaking to imagine what might be happening to yet another innocent victim.

They tried to listen to the radio to keep abreast of events but the interference made it almost impossible. They constantly stared out of the window during day time but it brought only anguish. Law and order seemed to have disappeared on the streets and some of the local residents were now taking advantage of this situation. Mobs were going on rampages, looting the shops and setting fire to empty property. Buildings were being destroyed with no retribution for the perpetrators.

Maria was anxious to protect her daughter but fear for their futures intensified.

'It's over for us, we're all finished,' she cried to her husband one evening, in a moment of despair.

Francis constantly tried to remain positive, 'I hear whispers that the underground movement are planning to launch a revolt with the aim of recapturing the city.'

'Do you mean we might just be saved after all?' his wife asked.

'Let's hope so,' he replied with an uncertain smile, 'but it's all extremely secretive.'

Over the next few days, there was a revolt by the Tajna Armia Polska (Secret Polish Army) but it led to terrible repercussions. The Germans were so incensed, orders came for all civilians still living in the city to be either killed or removed to concentration camps.

On returning home from school one day in late 1942, fifteen year old Maria was horrified by the scene that greeted her. The ends of her street had been barricaded, by a large contingent of German tanks, plus a large presence of Nazi soldiers with fierce dogs. They were armed and as Maria approached them, she caught sight of the dull glint from their rifle butts, in the weak autumn sunshine. How was she going to avoid them for they appeared to be everywhere? Could she manage to reach home without being spotted? Women she knew well were crowded onto the pavement, sobbing uncontrollably. Some of her neighbours had young children in their arms, who were fortunately unaware of what was happening. Old men stood in isolation, dazed and silent.

There was no escape route. Maria was instantly terrified. She knew exactly what was happening as she had heard much talk of deportations. She stopped, paralysed with fear, watching in silence as the soldiers, with their instantly recognisable square helmets, were entering every house systematically, and bringing out all the inhabitants.

Suddenly she spotted an opportunity. If she skirted round the large crowd, she may be able to hide herself behind them and reach home. Her heart was beating frantically but it worked. With great trepidation, she managed to slip past the soldiers and enter her front door.

She found her mother rushing around frantically, flustered as she tried to gather some possessions but not knowing which to prioritise.

She instantly ran to her daughter and threw her arms around her, in relief.

'Maria! Maria! I'm so pleased you are still safe and home in time to be with me.'

'But what about father?' Maria asked anxiously, trying hard to staunch her tears.

'I don't know, I don't know,' her mother answered honestly, shaking her head. Supposing her husband to be still at work, she explained, 'He won't be aware of what is happening in the street, will ….'

Suddenly their conversation was interrupted by a loud knocking. Then the door burst open. Two armed guards immediately ordered them to go and assemble outside. Maria gripped her mother's hand. Her mother was shaking but trying hard not to display any emotion or make any sound. The two of them walked through the front door, carrying just a few simple essentials in a bag and went to join their neighbours. They met the eyes of others and although no-one spoke, they all understood. That moment, young Maria was locked in dread and felt herself unable to breathe. What was going to happen to them? Where were they being taken? And what of her dear father? Her precious father! How would he feel when he returned home and found them gone? She knew he would be so desperately anxious about them and yet there was no way of letting him know – that was too hard to bear. But, but at least she and her mother were together.

Then she felt herself being grabbed by the arm and forcibly taken onto a truck. For a minute or two, she lost sight of her mother and Maria felt herself panicking. Fortunately her mother spotted her and after some quick manoeuvring, with the help of kind neighbours, they were reunited.

'Stay close to me, at all times,' her mother urged, as they gripped hands.

But secretly she knew there wasn't any guarantee that they would be allowed to stay together.

She scanned the faces of her fellow passengers, many of whom she recognised. Most folk appeared relatively calm, realising there was nothing to be gained by resistance, yet everything to be lost.   Nearly all of them knew that if they expressed their anger, they would do so to their cost.

Some young children were crying but most adults were simply stunned by fear, particularly an unspeakable dread of where they were going …for although they had no idea of their final destination, they knew, in the pit of their stomachs, that it would hold unimaginable horrors.

CHAPTER 17
BUCHENWALD - 1943 – 1945
ITALY – 1945 – 1947

The two of them continued to cling to each other as they journeyed to the outskirts of their devastated city and beyond. The destruction was immense and they found it overwhelming to see so many beautiful landmarks within the city, raised to the ground. It appeared that the magnificent palaces had simply been obliterated and its magnificent libraries were now burnt out shells, meaning thousands of books, maps and archives were lost forever. It was a surreal picture, almost akin to a silent horror movie.

Their endless journey took them westwards; it seemed as if time stood still before they finally arrived at a transit camp in Durchgangslager 121 in Pruszkow. Here, they were off loaded onto transit wagons to continue their journey. The night sky had arrived when they finally entered a concentration camp, just eight kilometres outside Weimar, in eastern Germany. Hidden in a beech tree forest was the formidable 'Buchenwald' – established in July 1937 as one of the seven main German concentration camps, although it was not classed as an extermination camp. Maria's mother had heard talk of this place and it instantly conjured up absolute horror in her mind. She tried hard to stay composed for the sake of her daughter but she had some idea of the cruel atrocities that were awaiting them.

All these latest inmates looked exhausted, bewildered and terrified as they were shunted through the gate. It was emblazoned with the slogan 'Jedem das Seine' literally translated as 'to each his own' but more figuratively as 'Everyone gets what he deserves.' Maria's mother tried to ignore its stark message as she pulled her daughter close, ever fearful that they may be torn apart.

To begin with, all the new detainees were taken through a reception procedure, carried out at double speed. Maria's mother was convinced the whole system was deliberately meant to bewilder and dehumanise them. The guards constantly shouted orders, swishing their whips to instil fear. They used fierce yelping dogs to further pacify the already traumatised newcomers. After each person was documented and photographed, came the humiliation of being given an individual number. Worst still, they watched in despair, as their personal possessions were confiscated.

Maria glanced up at her mother, as the soldiers snatched her bag but again Maria tried not to react. Inside, it felt they were taking away all vestiges of their personality and all traces of their identity. Were they no longer human beings but simply discardable objects of no value?

Next, they were herded in groups, into a stark room for 'decontamination'. Just exactly what would that entail, the young Maria wondered, but daren't ask. She simply followed orders.

First came the shaving of her body hair – everywhere. For a teenage girl, fresh into puberty, the embarrassment of displaying her private areas was intense. At that point, she bowed her head, avoiding eye contact, as the guards ran their primitive hand shears over her naked flesh. They left her soft skin feeling sore and in certain areas, she was bleeding from open cuts. The guards laughed and joked with each other as they worked, totally indifferent to the suffering and degradation of this new inmate who they considered a 'nobody.'

Maria studied them hard. Their features seemed unremarkable – their appearance quite ordinary yet the fear they injected in her was immense. She caught sight of one particular guard touching a youngster inappropriately whilst the girl squirmed but was too sacred to say anything.

Maria knew nothing of 'sexual assault' but she was acutely aware that his actions were unacceptable yet nothing could be said or done. She found herself shaking and feeling strangely ashamed, despite having done nothing wrong. She looked to her mother for reassurance but her mother appeared equally ill at ease and both were immensely relieved when the process was over at last.

Next came the allocation of an ill- fitting pair of clogs, plus simple clothes- all identical apart from size. The 'uniform' consisted of a simple striped outer garment, with coloured patches to denote the category of prisoner. It smelt repulsive, with an odour of vomit and faeces.

With procedures complete, Maria and her mother were now escorted to the women's barracks which were to be their new 'home'. As Maria marched towards the wooden structures, she was struck by the awful smell that filled the air. It appeared to be coming from a large chimney which towered above the large brick building, in the central area of the camp, dominating the skyline. It was an intense, burning smell. Fortunately, she had no exact idea of the cause and was reluctant to ask.

As they marched through the huge camp, they passed hundreds of fellow prisoners, varying in age and infirmity but all appeared depressed and half starved. Over the following days, as Maria studied their behaviour and listened to their language, she came to realise that the prisoners were from all over Europe – including the Soviet Union, and comprised both Jews and non-Jews, the mentally ill, the disabled, criminals and many political prisoners. Plus there were a large number of   homosexuals – not that Maria realised that – for this group of people were particularly hated by Hitler.

On entering the wooden barrack, the stark reality of their situation became apparent. It was certainly not designed to offer comfort. The one room was dark and poorly ventilated, with a small stove which was obviously totally inadequate as there was a distinct chill in the air. There was little in the way of furnishings, except for several wooden benches, each covered with one very threadbare blanket. Both Maria and her mother were allocated a bench, one above the other.

Food that night consisted of a small portion of dry bread and watery soup with very suspect contents. It seemed to barely touch their hunger.

'It seems like it's filled with saw dust,' Maria whispered.

'It probably is,' came the reply.

'We'll die of starvation in three months,' another prisoner remarked.

'That's the intention,' a long standing inmate replied bleakly.

The following morning they were awoken before dawn by a siren and ordered outside for a roll call. As they stood in long columns, Maria witnessed dreadful punishments being metered out on the weak and the vulnerable, by some of the more brutal SS men. No-one was referred to by name – for they were no longer classed as unique individuals but instead they were identified simply by their number. For some, particularly the Jews, this was tattooed on their arms but for most, it was written on their striped shirts.

Maria came to realise that within the camp there was a definite hierarchy, even amongst the prisoners. The criminal element – known as the *kapos* – were dominant, having authority over those who were regarded as lesser men and women. These men were particularly brutal and violent. Maria came to fear them more than the German guards. Over the coming months, Maria witnessed things that she was never able to talk about to anyone, then or in the future. Appalling sights and horrific sounds filled her young mind which left her traumatised.

Every day became hours spent full of uncertainty and fear – what would they bring? What horrors would they have to endure? Each day, they were expected to march to work in a local armaments factory, where they assembled weapons and others objects of warfare.

'In step, march, sing!' the guards ordered as they set off early every morning. En-route they repeated German songs, over and over again, almost to the point of stupefaction. Anyone not knowing the words or who sang too softly or dared to refuse was immediately given a beating. On their return journey each evening, the same tunes were sung until the words became ingrained in Maria's memory. By night time, as she lay on her bunk, she found herself reciting them unintentionally. Would the words ever go away?

After working long, exhausting hours, there also came a repeat of the dreaded roll call. This too was often accompanied by the same monotonous singing, usually naïve folk songs but on occasions some with obscene texts. It became incredibly annoying, along with the added tension of the count.

On many nights, the same thing happened. Maria watched nervously as the guards did their count, hoping the total would match the one in the morning. Invariably it didn't, for there was always someone who had died during the course of the day who needed deducting from the final tally. Another human being who had simply become a statistic; a man, woman or child who'd been shot, succumbed to sickness or committed suicide. Either way, their life now meant nothing and they were instantly forgotten by their captors. Most were not even given a decent burial. But whilst individuals were insignificant, correct numbers were essential.

As Maria stood, weary and hungry, once more the familiar cry of the commanding officer echoed around the main square.

'Again, count again,' he bellowed.

She knew, only too well, that sometimes this repetition could last well into the night, if numbers weren't correct. Afterwards, food became a very welcome relief, although it was totally inadequate and never palatable.

Maria constantly worried how she could cope with the constant gnawing that gripped her stomach, every minute of her waking hours but her main fears were now centring on her ailing mother. She watched in despair as, day by day, her mother became sicker. She became painfully thin, apart from her extended stomach and total exhaustion overwhelmed her. Gradually, her intense hunger crippled not just her body but her mind too. Her spirit seemed to be breaking as slowly she became more detached from what was going on around her and she barely spoke. She found it almost impossible to work and many times she stumbled, provoking a tirade of abuse.

Maria watched as her mother, so desperate now for any sustenance, tore up grass to chew, despite the fact such actions were totally forbidden. She realised her mother needed urgent medical attention but where would such help come from? If only her father was around, he'd know what to do and this thought truly haunted her. How she longed for him to appear; every time there was a new batch of arrivals she would scan their faces, desperately hoping he was among them.

She knew of no-one to whom she could turn. A few guards feigned kindness but Maria quickly realised they weren't to be trusted. As for her fellow prisoners, they were each focused on their own survival and had no strength to support others. So, despite her youth, she endeavoured to do whatever she could, to support her mother.

'Keep going mother, don't give in,' she begged, though she knew her words were ineffective. She took hold of her mother's limp hand and saw in her unresponsive eyes that she had lost all hope. This was too heart- breaking, too unbearable. Tears flowed and Maria felt desolate.

She looked around and saw all the naked bodies lying everywhere, unattended – no-one seemed to care. So many captives had succumbed to typhus and she feared for the future, for both of them.

News spread through the camp that someone had desperately tried to escape but they were soon caught. On their return, everyone was forced to watch as they were hung from a tree, although Maria lowered her eyes to avoid the final seconds. It certainly stopped most prisoners from any thoughts of doing the same.

Over the following days, Maria had to witness her mother succumbing to the final depravities of starvation. She became unrecognisable as her features changed; her body reduced to an empty shell, unable to communicate or carry out basic life functions. Despite the agony of watching her weaken, Maria was still forced to go to work.

In the end, she almost felt relieved when her mother took her final breath. At least now she was free from her suffering. Yet the pain of her loss was immense and beyond description.

It was a living nightmare with no escape. Maria just couldn't comprehend what had led to this. Her family weren't Jews. They weren't criminals. They weren't even pro -Russian. They were simply Polish. Why should that condemn them to death? Surely it would be her turn very soon.

She had no idea of how to cope with the enormity of what faced her. For as she looked around the camp, she realised she was totally alone, with no other family members. An orphan but not just an orphan, she was without relative or real friend, with no-one to comfort her. Tears flowed but there was anger too. This gave her a steely determination to live, believing that was the best way to honour her mother's sacrifice.

Over the endless months that followed, each day she survived seemed like a victory. Her thoughts constantly turned to her father. Had he also been captured and taken to another concentration camp. Was he possibly still alive? Would she ever find him again, if he was fortunate enough to keep safe and stay alive? That thought alone gave her an incentive to focus on her own survival.

Most of the guards were brutal and unkind but there were one or two who seemed to display a more human side and showed concern towards her, on occasion. Maria found for that brief moment she felt uplifted and it enabled her to stay strong. She willed herself to carry on and although the situation was so grim, she grasped at anything to lift her spirits.

Then, when almost at the limit of her endurance, on April 11th 1945, a miracle happened. At least that's what many inmates felt, including Maria. For news filtered through the complex that troops had arrived from the USA. It was whispered that they had come to liberate the camp.

'We are to be freed!' someone cried in joy, trying to pass the news around his fellow prisoners.

Most were too shocked by this and so disbelieving, they carried on as normal. Others were so ill they were beyond caring. Some were so frightened; they hid in their living quarters, like timid animals. Many expected the enraged guards to carry out vengeful acts in response. However, what they hadn't realised, on the day of liberation, an underground prisoner resistance organisation had seized control of Buchenwald, intending to ensure there were no such atrocities by the retreating camp guards. Some of the stronger prisoners even took hold of some guards and threw them into a pool of water, kicking them back in, until they drowned.

As they walked among the twenty thousand prisoners, the American soldiers were so shocked by what greeted them; many were reduced to uncontrollable tears. They couldn't take in the appalling sight before their eyes – the unspeakable conditions, the piles of corpses, the emaciated bodies of those still alive and the large number of children who seemed old beyond their years.

One of the young soldiers walked up to Maria, kindly offering her his hand and holding out some chocolate. She was shocked, never having seen a black man, but she trusted him and tried to smile, although it seemed she had forgotten how to. She gently laid her head on his outstretched arms. His face was kind whilst his heart was breaking.

Maria took the chocolate but she felt as if she was dreaming. Dare she eat it or would it be snatched away from her? Slowly as the reality of the situation sank in, those with enough energy ran outside the camp, breaking down the fences, no longer fearing reprisals.

The soldiers, seeing how ravenous the prisoners were, offered them tins of meat.

'What's this?' some asked suspiciously.

'Bully beef,' the soldiers said as they showed them the contents.

'What's bully beef?' the children asked as they crowded around, eager for anything to eat.

Some prisoners ate it with relish but many were soon bringing it back up. Their stomachs could not cope with the richness of it.

Maria was gently led out of the camp, along with other orphan children. A soldier spoke to her in Polish.

'You are going to be taken to a displacement camp in Barletta in Italy.'

Maria was rather bemused and disappointed not to be going 'home', although she doubted that she had either a family or a home to return to. It was so very hard to leave without her mother and the guilt she felt, knowing she'd survived whilst her mother hadn't, was immense. But for now, she felt immense relief to be leaving the camp and on her journey to freedom, even if it was to be found in Italy.

However, she did have one pressing concern.

'What exactly is a displacement camp?' she asked, fearing that she might be going from one concentration camp to another.

'It's where you will be looked after properly and they will help you regain your health and strength,' the soldier explained.

Maria, with her natural fortitude, accepted his explanation but was her ordeal finally over?

Barletta was located near the seaport of Bari, on the south-eastern coastline which formed the 'heel' of the country of Italy. The camp was run by the Polish Second Corps Army - not that Maria was to know the significance of this on her arrival. She quickly discovered that the layout of the camp was little improvement to the German equivalent. It comprised of endless rows of bleak, brick buildings, all with corrugated rooves which faced onto a bare street. There was little in the way of vegetation or trees to enhance their surroundings. The food also continued to be limited and the living conditions were rudimentary. But on the plus side, the weather was markedly different. It was good to feel the warmth of the sunshine compared with the damp, dull conditions faced back in Germany.

Once again, Maria was accompanied by men, women and children of different races and religion. There was a large element of Jews, many of whom were eager to travel on to Palestine for a fresh start. But at least here, Maria acknowledged, they were no longer classed as prisoners.

Both Maria and her fellow Polish detainees had their thoughts focused on a return to Poland. If there was any chance, however slim, she longed to be back in Warsaw, ever eager to find out what had happened to her father. But in the following days, there came constant discouragement from any thought of returning to their homeland. Posters were placed throughout the camp, displaying a mouse in Italy, looking at a mousetrap in Poland.

Throughout her stay, Maria was encouraged to attend vocational courses where she learnt new skills. She was also determined to make a real effort to learn the Italian language and began to test her skills on the locals. With time, she grew in strength and confidence and slowly blossomed into an attractive young woman, although a deep sadness was permanently hidden within her.

After almost two years at the camp, the time came for her to move on. But with an uncertain future and no great plans in her head, she was willing to follow instructions. She had no idea that the strong advice she was about to be given would have such a profound effect on the rest of her life.

'Try to erase everything that has happened to you. Be pleased instead that you have survived and put this experience behind you.'

These words resonated around Maria's head.   Believing that this suggestion was sound and sensible, she gave it much thought. Gradually over time, in the innocence of youth, she stored it deep within her subconscious mind. She would, she told herself, never share her terrible experiences with any other human being but instead she would keep the secrets of her horrific ordeal, locked away in her mind, forever remaining unspoken words. She longed to believe that her father might still be alive but felt it best if she accepted the likelihood that she was all alone in the world. Maybe it wasn't a good idea to try to return to Warsaw after all. Her indomitable spirit told her that she mustn't be overcome by her circumstances and she MUST NOT allow the Germans to take her future away, as well as her past. She intended to create a career for herself and maybe meet a man with whom she would like to begin a new family.

With that objective, in 1947, Maria joined four thousand other refugees and travelled by train overland to access England. She would begin her new venture in the capital city of London for it was surely an ideal place to start. Now she was resolute, determined that whatever she faced in the future, it could surely never be as bad as what she had gone through under the Nazis. ….

CHAPTER 18
MANCHESTER - 1958

'I've found a lump in my breast,' Maria divulged to Kazik, after several weeks of keeping this news to herself. She had hoped it might have disappeared with time, but unfortunately it hadn't. Not wishing to worry her husband, she quickly added, 'I don't expect it will be anything serious as I'm only thirty-one, it's perhaps just a cyst.'

At a loss to know how to reassure her, he said very little but in truth he was worried. On her next shift at the hospital, Maria decided to confide in a couple of her fellow nurses. They immediately advised her to chat with one of the consultants. After doing this, he referred her to the relevant surgeon who organised a biopsy straight away. She was relieved to be given what she deemed as priority treatment but was not expecting the difficult news that came next.

'Maria, we have your results and I'm sorry to tell you we've found cancer in your left breast. It's quite aggressive so you will need a single mastectomy,' the consultant gently informed her.

Maria, shocked by this news, barely took in his words. But he hadn't finished.

'We are also concerned in case the cancer has spread, so we will also need to remove your lymph nodes, under your arm.' Wishing to soften the blow, he then added, 'Be reassured, your age is on your side, you have a good chance of recovery, especially if you agree to the invasive surgery.'

The news was far worse than Maria had anticipated but she was grateful for his honesty and that she wouldn't have to wait long for treatment. She went home and broke the news to Kazik. His reaction was just what Maria expected. He made little comment but over the coming days, he became subdued and unresponsive. Maria, not wanting to alarm the children, simply told them she was unwell and that they would be having a small holiday. Then she set about making the necessary child care arrangements, realising Kazik wouldn't be able to stay at home to look after them whilst she was hospitalised.

She was extremely grateful when George and Edna Hawk kindly offered to have Sandra and Danny. As for Kazik's welfare during her absence, she accepted that she couldn't concern herself too much with his needs, he would have to fend for himself.

Within two weeks, Maria was given surgery. She slowly recovered from the operation but found adaptions had to be made which were very hard at first. Her initial concern was whether they had caught the cancer in time or if it would return in the future. She then decided this was a pointless worry, as she could do nothing to alter it.

Her next issue was coming to terms with her distorted appearance. She recoiled as she stared down at the dark pink, jagged scar on the now totally flat surface, marking where her left breast had once been. How would Kazik feel when he looked at her? Would he still desire her, for surely she had lost her attractiveness? The best option was never to allow him to see her naked, so she made up her mind to hide herself every bedtime, by undressing in the bathroom. Additionally, every morning, in order to improve her outward appearance, she placed some soft foam padding in her empty left bra cup.

Losing what she perceived to be her femininity was traumatic but her hard childhood in the concentration camp had taught her to be stoical and accepting of all situations. There was nothing to be gained from complaining, so despite this loss of her figure, she slowly dealt with it in her usual passive way. Instead of talking it over with anyone, she kept quiet and tried her utmost to carry on as normal.

After a period of rest, she was eager to return to work and even considered a new job working at the local Ann Coates Hospital. However, she soon realised her limitations, finding the daily chores of making beds, lifting patients and such like too intensive and too demanding physically. Constantly weary, she was now so restricted in what she could do. Her upper body muscles had weakened, as a result of the operation, causing extra difficulty when trying to help the more incapacitated patients. After several weeks of struggling, her employers advised her to look for alternative employment.

This was a real blow and not the news she wanted to hear, especially after all her efforts to build a successful and fulfilling career in nursing. However, once more, Maria was determined not to be beaten. She dealt with it just as if she had been dealt a few new cards to incorporate into a bridge hand. She wouldn't fret over it, for she had overcome far, far worse things in the past. Realising she had always had a flair for numbers, she opted to retrain as an accounts clerk, acknowledging that it was far less physically demanding.

It wasn't long before she gained employment at a local business and quickly made a success of this new venture. She told herself, her nurses' training wouldn't be wasted, knowing only too well that in family life accidents and illness were inevitable, especially with two lively children.

Sure enough, seven year old Danny came home from school one day complaining of feeling most unwell. Seeing his flushed cheeks and feeling how hot and sweaty he was, Maria realised he had a high fever. His chest was wheezing badly and her instinct immediately told her he needed prompt medical attention. The doctor diagnosed acute pneumonia and prescribed regular anti - biotic injections. Whilst Maria felt well qualified to give them, he certainly wasn't so keen to have them. She came up with a simple solution.

'I'll give you three pence, every time you have a needle,' she promised as a bribe.

Danny was soon having them without a fuss and slowly he made a good recovery. If only Kazik's health problems could be solved so easily, Maria mused. Despite taking regular medication, his mood could change without warning and he never seemed to be settled.

The Prime Minister, Harold Macmillan, had recently told the country that 'They had never had it so good,' with the post war economic boom. Certainly, Kazik recognised that within his own industry, coal mining, the rate of production was on the rise which meant an increase in wage and a higher standard of living than he could ever have expected in Poland. Yet despite the benefits, he refused to accept England as 'home'. He was relentless in his determination to maintain both his and the children's polskuse, their Polish national identity.

In his eyes, neither the English nor the Scottish people had ever accepted him, let alone liked him. In his mind they always treated him as an outsider, a foreigner and it would, he felt sure, never be any different. What did they know of the horrors he'd endured in the gulag, his bravery on the battlefield or his heroic actions at Monte Cassino? How would anyone begin to understand those years of suffering which still haunted him, when they didn't acknowledge or weren't even aware of his valuable contribution, aiding the British Army in their defeat of the Germans. In fact he still felt the injustice of what he deemed as a betrayal by the British government when they'd made a pact with Stalin. And as for his dream of visiting his homeland, it seemed to be simply that – a pipe dream.

Maria, on the other hand, constantly tried to ignore Kazik's negativity and endeavoured to remain upbeat. Eager to encourage the family to relax and lift the underlying tension, she came up with an idea.

'Why don't we purchase a puppy?' she suggested.

The children were delighted at this proposal whereas Kazik was not so keen. He was concerned by the work involved and unsure how he would respond to a dog, having never owned a pet. Finally after much coercion, he relented.

'Shall we call him Teddy?' Maria suggested when she brought home a small chocolate- coloured mongrel and looked into his cute brown eyes.

The children agreed and Teddy was instantly adored. For Sandra, particularly, it marked the beginning of a love and compassion for all animals that would follow her into adulthood. Even Kazik, who had shown such reluctance, was won over and offered to make it his responsibility to exercise him on a daily basis. Maria was sure this would be beneficial for both of them

. It wasn't too long before Teddy was joined by further pets, including a canary.

'Let's teach him to sing,' suggested Kazik as he peered into the canary's cage. 'Or maybe he could even learn to whistle!'

'How can we train him to do that?' the children asked, eager to give it a go.

'I've an idea,' their father replied, as he went to put the kettle on. As the water boiled, the kettle whistled away, prompting Kazik to pick up the bird cage and place it next to the hob. The children roared with laughter, as day after day, this procedure was repeated. However, despite their father's gallant effort, the bird could not be coaxed.

Then one morning, the children came downstairs and were surprised to see an egg lying at the bottom of the cage. Shouting for their father to come and look, it was now Kazik's turn to be amused.

'No wonder I had no success. It's a little known fact but only male canaries can learn to whistle. I think our canary must be a she not a he!'

As the menagerie of animals grew and with both parents working full time, Sandra and Danny were expected to help with chores but as this usually meant a reward of pocket money, they didn't object too much. Sandra's job was to feed and clean out the animals which by this time included a hamster, tortoise, mouse, rabbits and some gold fish. Every Saturday there was also housework to be done, including cleaning the wooden floor in the living room. It caused great merriment as they polished the linoleum floor with dusters attached to their shoes, skating around to make it shine. If they finished in good time, Kazik was willing to sit down with Danny and watch the television, particularly if his team 'Manchester City' was on 'Grandstand'.

Maria and the children really appreciated such times when they could laugh and watch their father joining in the fun. When he was relaxed, the children could relax too. They didn't need to be fearful that he might have an angry outburst or become totally withdrawn. More and more Maria could see that it was his illness alone that made him difficult. When he was feeling well he could be a kind and loving father and when they worked together, they enjoyed a contented and harmonious family life.

Maybe, the worst is nearly over, Maria pondered, ever the optimist. Hopefully, the flash backs and the horrific dark thoughts are diminishing and he can regain some happiness from everyday life and see a more positive future. Or was this another pipe-dream?

CHAPTER 19
MANCHESTER - 1959

Kazik continued to follow the political events in his Polish newspaper with great interest and for once he felt genuine excitement. He was starting to realise that travel to and from Poland was becoming easier and a visit to his homeland may no longer be out of the question. In fact he'd heard something of great interest, during a recent visit to the local Polish club. Apparently, the Catholic Institute were providing summer camps for young people, even offering to make arrangements for the children to travel independently and stay over with their Polish relatives.

This gave him an idea and after some thought, he announced to the children, 'You're both going to visit Poland.'

'What? Just us two?' Sandra asked innocently.

'Yes. Just you and your brother,' her father answered rather sternly.

Although rather shocked and bemused by this, neither Sandra nor Danny liked to question their father's decision. Why wasn't he or their mother going to accompany them? Yet they knew it was pointless to expect any explanation. He would never discuss such issues and what he said, had to be obeyed. As they were only ten and nine, Sandra felt a certain trepidation at just the idea of travelling all that way unaccompanied, especially as she felt the responsibility of being the older sibling.

As if reading her thoughts, Kazik continued, 'Your mother will take you to London airport to catch your flight and then your Aunt Eugenia will meet you on your arrival in Warsaw. It's all arranged.'

Sandra tried to be enthusiastic- it certainly sounded like an adventure and usually adventures were exciting, she told herself - but she had no idea who this Aunt Eugenia was or what Poland would be like.

Two days before their planned departure, all did not go quite to plan. On Kazik's return from work, he examined their travel documents and realised he'd made a mistake. He had misread the date of the tickets and actually the children were due to travel the

135

following morning. With great haste, the cases had to be packed, leaving Maria feeling rather upset, not having enough time to iron any of the children's clothes. She was always particular about such things but rather than complain to her husband, she held her counsel.

In the morning, Maria and the two children said a brief goodbye to their father, before catching their train to London. From there, they caught a connecting bus to the airport.

'Be good!' Maria ordered as she gave both children a final hug, before they boarded the aeroplane.

It was a tall, rather thin lady who met them on their arrival at the airport in Warsaw. After introducing herself as Aunt Eugenia, she gave both children an enormous hug and then stepped back, studying the two of them carefully.

'How much you look like your father- as I remember him,' she remarked as she spotted Danny's blonde hair and lean, tall stature. 'I guess you take more after your mother,' she added, looking at Sandra and noticing her darker, wavy hair.

She then explained, in Polish, that she was delighted to have them and how keen she was to introduce them to her family members. Some of her conversation was lost on the children but they smiled politely.

Together, they journeyed by car for several hours, until at last they reached the town centre of Zielona Gora, where they arrived at rather a drab tenement building, daubed with grey rendering. Yet, at the entrance stood the most beautiful pair of wrought iron gates, standing over six feet high and intricately decorated with floral patterns. Once inside the block, they walked through a central hall and turned right into their aunt's ground floor flat. Immediately they were greeted by members of her family.

'This is Halina, my daughter and Kazik, my son – they are similar in age to you two,' Aunt Eugenia explained as everyone gathered around the new arrivals.

'Kazik?' Danny repeated, smiling at the coincidence and with that the two boys began to converse with each other in Polish.

'Come follow me Olenka and Seweryn,' their aunt ordered, as she escorted them around the four roomed apartment and showed them where they were to sleep. Sandra quickly realised there was no bathroom but her aunt pointed out this wasn't a problem, as an old tin bath was used instead.

'And this is our toilet,' she explained, as they went outside the flat into a small closet within the hall, 'You will need a key to access it.'

Sandra was unnerved later on, when first visiting the toilet, to find herself locked inside. She shouted for help and was grateful that her cousin came to her rescue, explaining how to undo the bolted door. Afterwards, the incident became something that they both laughed about.

Over the coming month, Sandra and Danny enjoyed many new experiences, leaving little time to be homesick. They especially loved playing with their cousins and other neighbouring children, either outside on the cobbled street or in the communal garden behind the flat, which had a large pear tree at its centre. Aunt Eugenia also had her own small allotment, near the garden, where she grew the most tasty, sweet smelling tomatoes, which they were allowed to pick.

'I'm going to show you how to make bread dough,' their aunt informed them one morning. 'After we've made it, we'll have a trip to the bakers. As I've no oven, he'll bake it for me.'

After the visit, Eugenia took them to a local shop where they enjoyed some cake, although the tea which accompanied it was not so well received, due to the absence of any milk.

She also packed up delicious picnics for the children, as they went off to explore the local woods, with wonderful streams where they could fish and paddle or had hours of fun in an outdoor pool. Sandra found herself becoming particularly keen on Zbyszek, a lad of similar age to herself, not realising this was her first crush. When he presented her with some pears that he'd picked from the central tree, she couldn't have felt happier.

When Sunday came round, their aunt announced they were going to Mass. Sandra and Danny found themselves at The Church of our Lady of Czestochowa which was a beautiful building in the centre of the town. Once inside, their aunt whispered, 'I think it would be good for you to go to confession.'

Sandra felt nervous as it wasn't an experience she was too familiar with, however she spoke to the priest in English and he seemed impressed by both her attitude and that of Danny's.

'If English children can come to confession, then everyone should be able to,' he announced in his sermon later, making the two of them feel rather special.

The holiday was passing but there were still many new relations to meet for the first time.

'Your Aunt Werca and Uncle Jusek also live in the town and I know they're keen to meet you both,' their aunt explained.

Sandra found her Aunt Werca to be really friendly and lively and felt an immediate attachment to her. They were also pleased to have playmates, for she had two sons of similar age.

Next, Aunt Eugenia announced they were going to visit her younger sister, Aunt Jadwiga and her husband Uncle Zdiszlaw, who lived outside of Zielona Gora.

'They will be so pleased to meet you and you will love it, as they own a farm.'

'A farm!' Sandra and Danny chorused in delight. With both of them loving animals, they couldn't wait.

After a short journey by car, they pulled up outside a detached wooden house with a smallholding at the back. The sights and smells that greeted them were intriguing. Sandra watched carefully as her uncle showed her how he milked the cow. But when he offered her the chance to have a go, she lost her nerve and ran off. The day passed all too quickly and the holiday too was coming to an end.

On the final day, packing up seemed to take an age and the resulting delay meant they arrived at the airport late, causing them to miss their flight.

'We will just have to sleep in the airport waiting room, on a bench,' their aunt remarked casually but Sandra felt rather alarmed.

Seeing her niece's concern, Eugenia immediately tried to reassure them both.

'Don't worry, it will be just another story to tell your father when you get home.'

She was right, both Danny and Sandra had so much to relate on their return. It heartened Kazik – not only to hear news of their adventures but to know how much they had loved his homeland. It made him determined to save up, so that the children could go again. But next time he planned to accompany them, for he was desperate to be reunited with both his family and his beautiful country.

This decision did have its drawbacks for he recognised there were certain issues that needed facing. The expense was an obvious one, so he decided to pursue the idea of travelling by ship and train rather than flying, hoping it would be more affordable. But more pertinently, there were the many dark thoughts that so often filled his mind, taunting him with endless concerns. How would he cope with seeing his homeland again, after twenty years? Would it awaken chilling and painful memories? Would it still seem like home or would he be distressed by the many changes? How would he feel about seeing only some of his siblings? Would it remind him too much of those family members he had lost? Just how safe was it to return? Would there be any consequences, for he recognised that many parts of Poland were now under Russian domination. Since Stalin's death in 1953, the situation was less threatening but he was aware that it was not straightforward and he would need to apply for visas. Would he be granted them? The final, most pertinent issue, was Maria. Would she go with them?

Despite all these reservations, the following year, in 1960, Kazik decided he must procrastinate no longer. He began to plan his visit but despite much gentle persuasion, Maria continually refused to travel. It wasn't health issues that were holding her back – she seemed to have made a good recovery from her surgery- it was more a reluctance to return to her homeland. The stark reality for her, was no family of her own to visit, so there would be no joyful reunion to experience. She had had to come to terms with the fact that her father was undoubtedly dead, for she was certain he would have made every attempt to trace her, if he had survived the war. The pain of not knowing what had happened to him was unbearable and didn't need to be reawakened. This deep and lasting hurt, although left unspoken, was ever present and Kazik decided, in the end, rather than press her, to let the subject drop.

This time, Kazik decided to approach Fregata Travel Agency, recognised experts in organising such visits and within weeks the relevant documentation arrived. Suddenly, the reality of what was about to happen, made him rather apprehensive.

It was a beautiful summer's day when Kazik and the children finally set off but with the heat and the weight of their luggage, they found themselves struggling, as they loaded everything onto the train bound for London. They were pleased to find three vacant seats in a compartment where they could relax and catch their breath. Once settled, the children chatted endlessly in their excitement as they pressed their noses to the carriage window whereas Kazik was silent, apart from an odd rebuke, reminding the children to sit still.

On their arrival in the capital, they were joined by others travelling with Fregata to continue their journey to Harwich from where they caught the ferry to the Hook of Holland. Next came the long train ride across Europe and all three of them sat, rather subdued, as they became increasingly tired and hungry. The further they travelled, the more distant Kazik became and when the train finally crossed the border into Poland, his foreboding was evident. As his anxiety levels grew, his eyes became fixed with a blank stare, with his mind plagued by disturbing flash backs. How could he forget that time when he had travelled by train as a prisoner? He could still smell that pervading stench, he could still hear the terrifying growl of the guard dogs and he could still picture those awful scenes – hordes of desperate people crammed into the carriages and the horrific sight of all those lifeless bodies thrown onto the track. The horrors had never left him though he could never convey this to anyone, least of all to his Olenka and Seweryn.

Aware of his sombre mood, the children accepted his silence. Despite their youth, they knew only too well that it was best not to say anything. As they approached the town of Zielona Gora, Kazik tried to re-focus. He glanced out of the window and spotted wonderful trees and for a moment he was transported back to his childhood, when he had played with his brothers and sisters in a similar forest, sometimes collecting firewood and picking mushrooms. Yet the houses seemed so different – up until recently the town had belonged to Germany – and instead of typical Polish wooden buildings, he noticed there were many flats, built with brick and rendered with cement. What, he wondered, would the people living within them be like and how would they react to him? Soon he would find out, for now they had reached the station….

After leaving the train, Kazik tried to scan the sea of faces that were greeting all the arrivals. Suddenly, his heart skipped a beat. There standing before him was his younger sister, whom he immediately recognised as Eugenia. Never one to show his emotion, he kept his feelings in check, simply accepting her hug, whereas Eugenia could barely contain herself.

As she escorted him and the children into the car and back to her home, her increasing excitement was tangible. The house was full of relatives and as she rushed inside, she clapped her hands together, shouting,

'Look! Look! Kazik! Kazik! Twenty years! Twenty years! Who can believe it, it's twenty years since we saw him.'

One by one, all the family members hugged the arrivals and made their introduction.

'And this is your name sake, Kazik,' Eugenia said, as she ushered her son to greet his uncle.

Kazik was moved - to think she had named her son after him, some ten years earlier, when she must have believed her brother was probably dead. What a lovely tribute to him. Kazik, feeling reassured, now began to relax.

'Come and sit down, you must all be tired after your journey,' offered Eugenia's husband, Janek, trying to be practical.

'Perhaps though you are ready for something to eat?' Eugenia suggested as she led them to the table full of Polish treats.

Kazik accepted the glass of vodka offered to him with his meal. He truly appreciated being able to converse easily in his native language, so markedly different to life in Britain where every day was a struggle to make himself understood. It felt immensely comfortable to be amongst family members where you could be yourself, knowing you were accepted rather than judged.

He recognised they all shared a common bond; every one of his generation had endured unimaginable suffering in past years, although for the moment he concentrated on the present. He was pleased to see the children happy, as they played with their young cousins, giving the adults time to converse, although nobody brought up any issues from the war. Even over the coming days, the horrors they had experienced in the labour camps were barely mentioned. It seemed that it was something they all wanted to forget. Not easy when there were constant reminders of their ordeals, including their forced relocation from Zupran to Zielona Gora.

There were also his missing sisters: Renia, the oldest sibling and Maria. Kazik did enquire after them but Eugenia said very little.

'Renia is now living with her husband, Bolestaw, who's a farmer, with their five children in northern Poland. As for Maria, she chose to stay in Russia and adopt their way of life ....we have never seen her since,' she explained. Then she added rather poignantly, 'Although, I do receive a letter from her occasionally... and I know she is married with lots of children.'

Kazik accepted this news, without comment, although he found it hard to grasp why she would choose to be under Russian authority, especially as it meant no-one could travel to see her or meet her family. Eugenia had other sad news too, which she had chosen not to reveal in her letters to Kazik, fearing to upset him.

'I have to tell you that Wladek, your oldest brother is no longer with us. He died, in very sad circumstances, back in January 1952. He journeyed out into the snow one night and was overcome with hypothermia, despite being only thirty -nine.'

Kazik wondered if he had been drinking heavily at the time but he didn't like to ask. He shook his head in disbelief, wondering how much the war was to blame, but he chose to say nothing.

During his stay, Kazik also became aware that his sister Werca had a problem. Then he recalled Eugenia had alluded to it in that first letter. She appeared to have an obsession with her face. She endlessly checked the large mole on her cheek and would regularly seek out a mirror to make sure it was looking acceptable. Neither Kazik nor the children realised that the mole was actually hiding a much hated tattoo given to her by the Russian guards back in Siberia. It was a secret she wanted to hide from everyone.

However, regardless of their haunting memories, over the next couple of weeks, the family managed to enjoy some fun times together, much of it spent eating, drinking and visiting the local area. On one such occasion, when everyone was gathered at Eugenia's house, they were suddenly alerted to a commotion in the backyard. The cousins were all playing happily when Sandra became aware of a distressing cry coming from a drain cover. The cover was housed over a large sewerage pit which came from the nearby outside toilet. With her instinctive love of animals, she had a sense that the noise was something she wanted to investigate.

'Listen,' she said, speaking in Polish, as she beckoned the others to come over, 'It sounds like a young cat, it must be stuck,' pointing to the ground where they had all gathered.

'I think someone must have put a kitten down the toilet,' Kazik explained as he assessed the situation, after coming outside to investigate what all the fuss was about.

Immediately he set out to help, forcing open the drain cover and climbing down into the foul-smelling effluent below. Despite several unsuccessful attempts, he didn't give up. Finally, he managed to grab the scared animal, and lift it to safety. Then he set about cleaning it, washing it carefully and gently, before releasing it. Sandra felt so proud of him. Her father, the hero!

It was to be an incident that always stuck in her mind in the future. Whenever her father seemed agitated or showed any aggression towards her, she reminded herself that basically he was a kind and caring man and that was indeed a comforting and reassuring thought.

Before their holiday was complete, there was one final visit that Kazik was still desperate to make.

'Go get yourselves ready,' he ordered Danny and Sandra one morning. 'We're going to Wasilkow.'

'Wasilkow?' they repeated, having no idea where that was. Were they going to another farm, they wondered?

'No,' Kazik explained, 'it's a village about sixty kilometres from the Russian border.'

Just hearing the word Russian made the children wonder if it was a place they really wanted to go but once again they kept quiet. A long train journey followed, a distance of over seven hundred kilometres but the children accepted it, with some foreboding as to what or whom they were going to see. As for Kazik, he was feeling an intensity of emotions. This was going to be a momentous reunion. How would he cope?

His mind began to drift back to twenty years earlier, to that never to be forgotten day when he had been arrested. He recalled that his younger brother Janek, had been out at the time but he'd no true idea of what had happened to him after that. Kazik had so often thought of his younger sibling, for despite their eight year age gap, the two of them had had a special bond. How would Janek react at seeing his older brother again after all this time apart? He would soon find out.

Kazik ushered the children ahead as he finally located the correct address. As he approached the house, he let out a deep sigh.

'This is it,' he explained to the children, his voice almost breaking, 'this is my youngest brother's house - you are going to meet your Uncle Janek.'

With that, the door burst open and there he stood. He was shorter than Kazik with a head of thick, brown hair but he was still instantly recognisable as his brother. The two men stood without words for what seemed an age and then Kazik and the children were escorted inside to meet Janek's wife, Janina plus his two sons, Wiesiek and Romek and daughter Danusza. Feeling totally at ease, the two brothers began talking away in their thick Polish accents, with most of the conversation going over the children's heads. They spoke at great length. For the first time ever, Kazik felt able to share some of his blackest thoughts and to relate certain horrific sights he had witnessed during his incarceration. In turn, Janek shared his memories of those missing years and his hatred of everything Russian.

'I had a bad bout of typhus whilst fighting in General Sikorski's army at Poznan and reluctantly I was forced to leave. This caused me great frustration and disappointment... I so hated the Russians and all they stood for.'

Kazik was keen to reassure him, 'You played your part Janek, many soldiers suffered similarly, it wasn't your fault you became ill. I'm just pleased you survived.'

'Yes, and I found a wife too. We moved to Wasilkow to be nearer to Janina's parents. I'm content now, building bridges for the railway and keeping coypu....'

As his voice trailed off, he turned to his brother. He had a probing question he was really keen to ask, 'Do you think you and Maria would consider coming back here permanently? I'm sure you'd be really happy living in Poland once again.'

Kazik was at a loss to know how to respond. He would love to return to his own homeland but he recognised that Maria had made a new life for herself in Britain.

'Maybe one day, one day,' he said with feeling but in reality he doubted whether Maria would ever agree to it.

All too soon the visit was over and it was time to return to Eugenia's. As they said their goodbyes, the two brothers were both determined that this wouldn't be their last meeting.

'I hope you will be able to visit us in England one day,' Kazik suggested, although he appreciated this would be difficult.

'Yes and you must come back and bring Maria next time,' Janek insisted, 'and even find a house over here.'

Kazik smiled but he hadn't liked to disclose that Maria hadn't wanted to come, even for a visit. Eugenia was equally determined that they return, telling her brother so, when his visit came to an end.

'Please keep in touch and don't wait another twenty years before you come back!' she said as she waved them off.

'Thank you for everything,' Kazik responded, trying to smile, hoping to hide his true feelings, for the visit had affected him profoundly. A deep longing filled his heart but it was not to be shared or spoken of to anyone....

CHAPTER 20
MANCHESTER - THE 1960s

On their return to Manchester, family life returned to normal ....for a while at least. Kazik worked hard with his eight hour shift patterns at the colliery whilst Maria continued to supplement the family income with her work as an accountant.

Occasionally, she would abandon her tight rein on the budget and allow the children a treat, such as taking them to the pictures. Equally, ever keen to benefit them educationally, she encouraged them to read books, chosen from the weekly visit of the mobile library.

She was also eager for them to acquire another dog. Teddy had long since died and they all missed him. One weekend, she took Sandra out to a breeding kennel in Salford and together they chose a Cairn terrier puppy .On their return, they crept inside the house, went upstairs and discovered Kazik asleep on his bed. Maria gently laid the puppy next to him. He was soon woken with the puppy's antics.

'Who's this?' he enquired as he became aware of having his face licked.

'I thought it would be good for us all to have a new puppy,' Maria said, hoping he would agree.

Kazik was unsure but it wasn't long before he was persuaded that 'Beauty' was a great idea. Taking him for daily walks was a good chance to relax, out in the fresh air.

Generally speaking, Kazik was stable, although all of the family recognised that he didn't like to be challenged and his moods could change without warning. This tended to keep the children on tenterhooks, unsure of his reactions.

When Maria and Kazik were busy at work, the children were usually left alone for a short period after school.

'Don't you two be fighting!' their mother warned, 'if your father finds out he won't be at all pleased.'

In truth, Sandra and Danny did usually end up arguing yet they would invariably display a united front to their parents.

One afternoon, Danny and Sandra were playing alone in the living room when they spotted a sixpence, lying on the mantel piece. Not thinking of the consequences, they decided to take it, intending to use it at the first opportunity, to buy some sweets or maybe go swimming at the local baths.

When their father arrived home from his early shift, he soon spotted the coin was missing.

'Have you two seen a sixpence that I left here this morning?' he queried, immediately suspicious that they were the culprits.

Danny spoke up for them both, whilst Sandra looked on anxiously as he concocted his story.

'Yes, we did play with it dad but I'm sorry to tell you, we accidentally dropped it in our bedroom and it rolled under the skirting board. There was no way we could retrieve it.'

Kazik, doubting the truth of this explanation, especially as they had told him they'd lost the coin upstairs when he knew it to be left downstairs, wouldn't let the matter drop. But rather than be angry, he adopted an alternative strategy.

The children, looking at each other for reassurance, watched as he went to the cupboard and pulled out his torch.

'Follow me,' he commanded as he climbed the stairs to the relevant bedroom. As the two of them stood in the doorway, they waited whilst their father knelt on the floor and for the next twenty minutes, meticulously went up and down, sweeping the torch backwards and forwards, along every inch of the skirting board, shining the light into every crack and crevice, looking for the coin.

Danny and Sandra observed in complete silence. Knowing as they did, that he would never find the coin, both of them became increasingly jittery. As the minutes ticked by, they began to weigh up their options. Should they own up to the theft and face their father's definite wrath? Or should they remain silent? What would his reaction be when he finally gave up? The atmosphere was tense but Danny took the lead and opted to say nothing.

'Well, it's definitely not under the skirting board,' their father remarked, staring straight at their red faces. He had such a punishing stare it almost seemed to bore a hole straight into them.

What were they to say now? Both simply shook their heads with puzzled faces, hoping to keep up the pretence of their innocence but were secretly dreading what was going to happen next. Would punishment come later?

But Kazik was wise. He simply went back down stairs, replaced the torch in the drawer and carried on as normal. Even though he never spoke of it again, he knew he didn't need to. He'd made his point and he was sure they would never do such a thing again.

For Sandra and Danny, the incident left a lasting impression... for whilst Kazik was the usual mix of both a strict yet loving father, they also recognised that he was very unpredictable which was very confusing. Sometimes he seemed incapable of coping with simple things going wrong whereas at others, he took things in his stride. Certainly, they were learning to avoid actions which might incite him to anger although it was hard when they had no idea what might trigger it. Simple irrelevancies, such as forgetting to close a sideboard door, would cause him to lose his temper, often resulting in an unnecessary outburst whilst other more serious wrongs – such as the stealing and telling lies-seemingly went unpunished.

Kazik and Maria were always frugal, constantly trying to keep a tight rein on their limited budget. So when an invite arrived to visit Seweryn and his family up in Dumfries, Kazik gladly accepted this very welcome offer of a holiday. As it was August and the long school break, Sandra and Danny were equally keen to go, although Maria had to decline due to work commitments.

After an endless train journey, they arrived at his large country mansion, set deep in the heart of the Scottish countryside and surrounded by a working farm with a large lake. Sandra, particularly, felt quite in awe as she ventured inside the huge eight-bedroomed house. This was luxury on a scale she had never experienced. She found it amusing that a gong was struck, when summoning them to their evening meal and that it was served by the cook, in a sumptuous dining room.

The daytimes that followed were spent playing with Seweryn's four young sons, riding their bikes, playing croquet on the lawn and taking in all the sights and sounds of the farm. Meanwhile, Kazik took the opportunity to relax with his friend, sharing a glass of wine, playing bridge and discussing political issues.

When the time came for them to return home, Seweryn had a surprise for Sandra and Danny. He presented them both with a brand new bicycle. They were quite overcome with his generosity and they simply couldn't wait to show them to their friends back home. For Kazik, the break had provided a welcome escape from his daily grind and he returned to Manchester in better spirits. It prompted him to think about a return visit to Poland; maybe he should start saving up and hopefully he'd be able to go back with his family, the following year......

1963 Wasilikow

Kazik was really appreciating being back in his homeland and spending time with his siblings. It was greatly satisfying to watch his 'Olenka' and 'Seweryn' mixing and conversing in Polish with their cousins. He was sad that once again Maria had declined to join them but he focused instead on his offspring, realising just how much they were growing up. He watched, with delight, as Wiesiek, Janek's son, taught Sandra to play the accordion and use spoons to make a tune, both fond childhood memories of his own. They were simple pleasures but to Kazik, it was giving her a love of Polish traditions which was so important to him. He returned home ever more determined his children remain 'Polish'.

However, this soon led to family tension, especially as Sandra and Danny, bowing to peer pressure, were now favouring a more English way of life. Every week, they loved watching Top of the Pops on TV but one evening, without explanation, their father simply walked over to the television and switched it off. When Sandra decorated her room with some brand new pop posters, he made a point of tearing them off the wall. Such actions had to be accepted without complaint.

Yet conversely, he would show moments of unexpected kindness. Sandra was keen to try her hand at cooking but initially, she was not always successful. After a failed attempt to make a Swiss roll, Kazik still ate her half- baked offering with relish and complimented her on what he thought was a wonderful pancake.

Sandra tried to take solace from such times, believing that he did care about her and that underneath the surface of this volatile man was a compassionate father. As she and Danny matured, they were becoming much more aware that their father wasn't a well man. They watched despairingly as once again, he descended into a totally delusional state. As he became evermore detached from life, he showed great reluctance to go to work. Every evening, he would pace around the living room or sit in his chair staring into emptiness, displaying a flat almost vacant expression.

That Christmas, an occasion when Kazik was usually on top form, his disturbed conduct continued. Danny and Sandra had clubbed together to buy their father some drink but as he opened it, instead of thanking them as they expected, he simply cackled loudly, dismissing it to one side. The laugh was quite alarming to hear as it was more sinister than normal laughter, almost with a frightening rather menacing intonation.

Maria had always endeavoured to hide his condition from the two of them but now it was no longer possible. Yet these episodes went unmentioned, for Maria was constantly fearful of Kazik's reaction, especially if he thought the three of them were talking about him. Yet silently, they were all acknowledging that he was very ill and needed medical intervention.

Finally, early in the new year of 1964, Kazik's condition became so serious, with his alarming behaviour escalating, that it could no longer be ignored. Kazik's doctor agreed and suggested he be admitted into Salford Royal Hospital to receive treatment for depression and acute paranoia.

Maria tried to visit him as often as she could, take Sandra along with her but he was totally unresponsive at first. It was only after a fortnight of intense treatment that his mood started to improve. On their next family visit, with Danny agreeing to tag along, they were pleased to find him much calmer and he even suggested they have a game of table tennis.

'Come on let's see if I can beat you,' he challenged his son, managing a smile and together they enjoyed a few minutes of calm and normality.

After several weeks, Kazik was allowed to return home and resume family life. Maria could see he'd recovered when, after admitting she had completely mislaid her wedding ring, he didn't over react but merely accepted it, expressing neither anger nor disappointment.

The following day, he even asked Sandra to accompany him secretly to town in order to visit several jewellery shops.

'Try these Olenka - it will give me an idea of the correct size for your mother,' he asked, as the jeweller showed them various gold rings.

On returning to Maria, he presented her with a replacement ring. She was delighted with the gift but equally thrilled at this indication of how much he had improved.

But with two growing teenagers in the mix, family life was always destined to be a constant roller coaster. Danny particularly was causing a few problems and his clashes with his father were becoming more frequent. Kazik had always been immensely proud of his son, with great hopes and plans for his future, knowing

Danny had inherited great intelligence. He constantly pushed his son to achieve at school but this pressure wasn't going down well and led to much resentment. Danny started to rebel, missing lessons and misbehaving in the classes he did attend. When his end of year school report arrived, it highlighted just how much his behaviour had deteriorated, informing his parents that if things didn't improve, he would be expelled.

'*Will he ever grow up?*' – These words, hand written in the teacher's final comment, jumped out at Kazik and he reacted immediately, unable to reconcile that a son of his could let him down in this way. Didn't Danny appreciate all the many personal sacrifices his parents had made to give him the best education? Was this how he had repaid them?

The family fell silent as Kazik ordered Danny upstairs. Maria and Sandra hovered in the living room, fearing what was to come. They listened as Danny took a beating, the silence broken by his disturbing cries. Sandra looked nervously over to her mother, desperately hoping she would intervene, but she didn't. Why not, she wondered? Sandra found it so unbearable that the memory of it haunted her for years to come but again it was never spoken about, then or in the future.

Later in the week, the monks from the school contacted Kazik.

'We think you're maybe pushing Danny a bit too much,' they suggested.

But Kazik didn't see it like that. He felt he must have failed as a father and it brought back some difficult memories from his own youth. His parents had both died by the time he was eleven which had been incredibly hard but despite this, he'd been the only sibling to go to high school. In fact, he recalled his babunia had presented him with a gold watch at the time. He'd then gained a place at the military academy although unfortunately he had been unable to complete his training due to illness. He simply wanted better for Danny ….and from Danny.

Even worse was to come, for over the following weeks Danny showed no improvement in his attitude, resulting in him being permanently excluded from Xaverian College. He tried to find employment but his limited efforts were unsuccessful, forcing communication between father and son to virtually cease. Kazik spiralled once more into his black hole, becoming totally withdrawn. It upset everyone but they hoped that if he was left alone, in time, he might revert to 'normal' and then he would be different again…..

In the summer of 1966, Sandra's seventeenth birthday was approaching and she was really keen to have a party. But in every decision, there was always a rider - how would this idea be received by her father? Perhaps the best option, she decided, might be not to tell him of her intentions.

After meeting up with her close friend, Lesley, they planned to hold a celebration when both Maria and Kazik would be working a late shift. Word of the party quickly spread.

'Sandra's parents will be out, do come,' their friends were told but they hadn't quite bargained for the way their invitation would begin to snowball. That evening, the house became full of noisy guests. Young men on scooters, the local 'mods' turned up and Sandra was mortified as more and more unruly teenagers arrived, many she didn't even know. Not only were the numbers becoming out of control, so was the behaviour.

Suddenly a panic stricken Sandra spotted her father walking up the drive, returning home much earlier than expected. The house emptied amazingly quickly but Sandra and Lesley waited in trepidation for the backlash, especially as they surveyed the upheaval all around them. Incredibly, her father said nothing. He simply helped her to clear up the mess and left it at that. What was happening? She couldn't believe she'd escaped punishment, especially on this particular occasion when she felt he had every right to be angry.

For despite her approaching adulthood, Kazik continually instilled strict discipline, even insisting that whenever she went out with friends, she had to be home by ten- thirty. She found this so difficult when the centre of town was a good thirty minutes bus ride away, which meant leaving events much sooner than her friends ever did.

One evening, close to her 18th birthday, after going to a disco, she mistimed it and as she approached home, she realised it was five minutes past her curfew. She ran breathless into the house, hoping for the best but fearing the worst. There, stood in the doorway, was her father. She knew instantly, from the dark look on his face, he wasn't going to let her get away with it but this time his reaction went totally beyond what she felt was acceptable. He instantly removed the leather belt from his trousers, grabbed her tightly and hit her twice, across her bottom. Sandra recoiled as the pain was intense, with the force of it leaving bright red welts on her 'cheeks'.

The following morning Sandra showed her mother the large bruises but whilst she nodded sympathetically, she said absolutely nothing, either to her or later to Kazik. Sandra was disappointed but she knew her mother was fearful of repercussions. Kazik's mental health was definitely worsening and it would soon bring far more trouble on the family than either of them could have imagined.

CHAPTER 21
MANCHESTER - 1968

'I'm thinking of going on holiday for a short while,' Kazik announced one morning in late July.

'On holiday?' Maria repeated tentatively, for recognising her husband was in one of his uncommunicative periods, she thought it might be best not to ask too many questions.

'I'd really like to go back to Poland again, especially to see Janek,' he explained.

Maria accepted the situation, knowing how important such visits were to Kazik. Yet she felt slightly uneasy, wondering how he would cope travelling alone, knowing neither Sandra nor Danny would be going with him this time. Sandra had recently moved out of the family home, having secured seasonal employment as a receptionist at Butlin's holiday camp on Barry Island, in North Wales. Although Danny was still at home, he was a typical seventeen year old and rarely surfaced, except at meal times and he certainly wouldn't wish to accompany his father on holiday.

Despite her misgivings, Maria realised time with his family was probably just what her husband needed, so she helped him with his packing and discussed his travel arrangements. On the day of his departure, Kazik seemed quite calm.

'Please tell Olenka, I'll be in touch with her soon,' he requested just as he was leaving.

'Keep in contact with me too!' Maria joked as she kissed him goodbye.

Over the following days, Maria found her situation difficult. Despite his solitary and often troubled nature, she genuinely cared about her husband and missed his presence. There were constant reminders wherever she looked– his trusty bicycle lying in the shed, his treasured wooden cigarette box, still placed on the mantel piece in the living room and his work clothes left in the wardrobe. She also found it tough without his weekly wage. She was upset that Danny displayed no urgency to contribute towards his upkeep whereas Sandra willingly sent some of her limited income.

As time passed, Maria started to become concerned. She hadn't heard from Kazik and wondered how much longer he was going to stay away. She didn't imagine that he'd taken enough medication with him to last for too much longer and this in itself was a worry. She knew just how important his tablets were in keeping him stable. Yet she kept reminding herself, he had a return ticket, indicating he was intending to come back … although, worryingly, it would surely be invalid soon.

Sandra too had her own unanswered questions. Just why hadn't her father returned? Was he too ill to travel? Was he deliberately staying away? But she kept such thoughts to herself, trying hard to remain positive, convincing herself that Aunt Eugenia would have let the family know if he was too unwell to travel.

A few days later, she discovered the answer to all her concerns. On her return to her chalet, after a late shift, she spotted an envelope on the doormat. Seeing the neat handwriting, she immediately recognised it as her father's. She opened it with trepidation. The words on the page leapt out at her, filling her with panic:

'I am not coming back … I have decided to stay here and make Poland my home. ….'

Sandra read the words repeatedly, trying to take them in. Did her father truly prefer to live in Poland without his family than stay in England and be close to his children? How could her father do this to them? Hadn't her mother faced enough loss and suffering in her life without having to cope with this abandonment? How would Danny take the news? The questions continued..

At that moment Sandra felt great emotional pain, utterly distraught at her father's decision. As her mind raced, her main thought was to try and persuade him that this was not a good idea. Hopefully, he was just having a low period and perhaps if she reasoned with him, he might choose to return. But there was a big drawback to this plan - she just didn't have the financial means to fund a trip to Poland.

When Sandra next met her mother, it seemed strange to her that nothing was said regarding Kazik's desertion. Sandra didn't like to be the one who brought it up, so she waited to see if her mother broached the subject. When she didn't, initially Sandra began to wonder if her father had even informed Maria of his intentions. But on reflection, it seemed far more likely, knowing her mother as she did, that she just wasn't willing to speak about it.

It was only later, when she heard her mother confront Danny, that she felt reassured.

'When are YOU going to look for a job?' Maria demanded, as frustration overwhelmed her, 'you need to be contributing to this family, the same as your sister, now your father's gone'

Danny didn't reply but her anger registered with him and he finally acknowledged that it was a problem which needed addressing.

Then, several weeks later, as the reality of the situation began to sink in, Maria openly expressed her concern – though not for herself- her anxiety centred on Kazik.

'What are we going to do corukna? (*a Polish endearment*) Your father's a sick man and he needs medical help but will he get it in Poland?'

'I'll arrange to go over to see him, as soon as I can raise enough money,' Sandra offered.

Maria was keen to do something immediately.

'I'll make an appointment with his doctor and talk over the whole issue with him.'

Sandra agreed this was a sound idea.

The doctor proved to be very supportive, listening patiently as Maria explained her predicament. He then responded, offering her sound, practical advice in a gentle but truthful way.

'If Kazik wants to stay, there's not much can be done to persuade him otherwise. But he'll definitely need support in Poland, with ongoing treatment for his condition. I'll put together a medical report which you can send to his relatives and then they'll be able to seek the correct help and care for your husband.'

Maria appreciated his frankness and she didn't have to wait long for his medical assessment.

'Here you are, would you like to read the report that the doctor wants us to send to Poland,' Maria asked Sandra a few days later.

Sandra studied it carefully, totally unprepared for what she was about to read. She'd recognised for a long time that her father was unwell mentally but to see his stark diagnosis, written down in black and white, almost paralysed her. Tears welled in her eyes. Was this truly the nature of her father's illness?

'Paranoid schizophrenia'

Suddenly it explained such a lot of the abnormal behaviour she had witnessed during her adolescence– the angry outbursts, the delusional ideas, the scary laughter, the irrational mood swings and the violent reactions. Now the truth of it was almost unbearable. At that moment, Sandra longed to visit her father and offer him her love and support.

No wonder her childhood had been difficult yet none of it was actually Kazik's fault or done deliberately. He had a debilitating mental illness, in the same way as some people have ongoing physical ailments. He hadn't asked to be ill, and no doubt, Sandra reasoned, all those months of suffering, whilst incarcerated by the Russians, must have contributed to his condition.

This revelation was a redefining moment for Sandra and a memory she would never erase. Her heart was heavy as she understood the seriousness of his mental state and its terrible consequences. What was to become of her father? In fact, what was the future for all of them?

Maria decided to forward the doctor's letter to Kazik's sister, Eugenia, requesting she pass it on to the relevant medical authority. She was trying hard to come to terms with the impact Kazik's decision would undoubtedly have on her future, realising her single status was going to be difficult, especially having sole responsibility for Danny. However, she was determined to display her usual resilience to life's battles. Rather than allow her troubles to overwhelm her, she would try to continue with life as best she could. Hadn't she survived worse trauma in the past?

Now there were a couple of important concerns which needed to be faced. Firstly, her lack of money, as a single wage-earner, was an immediate issue. Her pride -or was it simply ignorance - meant she wouldn't turn to social security for financial help. She was grateful for Sandra's contribution from her wages but she needed some help from her son too. And there lay a second issue, how was she going to explain to Danny that his father wouldn't be returning, knowing how badly he would react?

Her fears were justified. On being told, Danny was really angry at what he saw as his father's desertion. He needed his father around, although he wouldn't openly admit it. Nor did he feel able to provide the emotional or financial support that he recognised his mother would now require.

Over the coming days, he withdrew even more and began to disappear on occasions, without disclosing his whereabouts, only to return a few days later. It came as a real surprise to Maria, when he suddenly informed her, 'You'll be pleased to know I've found work …in a local bar,' but before Maria could express her gratitude, he added, 'and I'll be living in on the job. I'm moving out and going into Manchester city centre, near Albert Square.'

Maria certainly wasn't expecting that outcome and now she didn't know whether to be pleased and grateful that he'd found employment or more sad and slightly annoyed that he was leaving home and not around to support her. It was only after his departure, that she appreciated how much she missed his presence. Although he wasn't one for idle chatter, just having him around had been company, especially during the time Sandra had been working away.

Maria was feeling particularly dispirited, when she had unexpected visitors. Seweryn and his wife Elizabeth had travelled down from Scotland to see how she was coping. They came armed with a large amount of provisions and then on hearing of Maria's financial struggle, Seweryn immediately arranged to pay off her outstanding rent. His generosity went further, 'Why don't you come and spend a few days with us up in Dumfries?' he suggested, on their departure, a few days later. Maria gratefully accepted, realising a break away was just what she needed. It would give her lots of free time to consider her future.

On her return, she was grateful the Butlin's season was coming to an end, meaning Sandra could now re-join her. Sandra had found new employment, as a switchboard operator at CIS Insurance in Manchester, so she could continue to make regular contributions to the rent. Maria began to feel more positive but she was wondering how she could resolve the whole situation with Kazik. Should she divorce him or would this give her less financial security? Maybe she should try for a re-conciliation? But would this mean relocating to Poland and living there permanently?

She'd only recently signed a pledge of allegiance to Britain. Whilst Kazik had still been around, she'd gone to the British Consulate in Manchester and made her promises and been so proud to gain British citizenship. Kazik hadn't been too impressed with her decision but she had grown to like Britain and wanted to be accepted. She certainly couldn't contemplate leaving England, so if Kazik intended to make Poland his permanent home, she didn't want to be with him. Yet she doubted that he could ever be persuaded to return to England.

She decided to visit Kazik's consultant and express these concerns to him, even divulging the negative impact they were having on her own health. He listened to her story sympathetically. It wasn't the first time he'd heard of a Polish immigrant who'd struggled to cope with the cultural life of Britain and he realised, in this instance, he had to be totally honest about her future.

'I'm sorry to say this but I think you should try to forget your husband, as I doubt if he'll ever return. I think you may be better off adjusting to a life without him,' he concluded.'

Maria nodded in agreement, realising he'd verbalised what she'd known all along. It was difficult news for her to hear but it was sound advice. What other choice did she have? She accepted that he would never come back willingly but then to actually 'forget her husband' was, she felt, a step too far. She still cared deeply about Kazik and recognised that when he'd been well, he had been a loving husband and father. As a former nurse, she fully understood the horrors of mental illness; knowing the long lasting impact of the condition, not just on the patient, the family   were victims too. Equally, she knew it wasn't of his making. He hadn't chosen to be ill and he certainly hadn't wanted to be so unhappy.

Whilst Kazik had largely managed to hide his condition from the world, he certainly hadn't been able to hide it from her, nor from the children in latter days. She knew the torment that he'd faced but it was the detrimental effect it had had on their daily existence which she had found so hard to tolerate. He had been so unpredictable that it had created tension within the family. Sometimes he'd reacted violently over such simple things whilst at other times he'd withdrawn into an impenetrable shell and not been able to communicate with anyone. No wonder her nerves were frayed and in recent weeks, she'd had some worrying pains in her stomach which she put down solely to stress. But were they?

There was though, she decided, nothing to be gained from self -pity, she would make her decision and stick to it, then deal with it in the only way she knew – and that was never to speak of it - for what was past was indeed that and nothing would change it.

Now she must face the future with a strong determination to survive and do her best to support Sandra and Danny. Sandra, she felt, had the sort of personality to help her deal with this situation but Danny was different and much more of a concern. He seemed to have inherited some of his father's problems and although he was a lovely lad, he had issues which seemed to be surfacing now he was growing up... would he ultimately survive this?

CHAPTER 22
1969 - MANCHESTER

I've found work in Eastbourne, my corukna,' Maria suddenly announced at the beginning of 1969, without any prior warning for Sandra.

'Eastbourne?' Sandra repeated, totally shocked at this revelation. Why had her mother not mentioned such plans before? Now it appeared to be a 'fait accomplit.' Not only was she travelling to the other end of the country, where was her mother intending to live and where did that leave Sandra?

'I've found work in a hotel as a manageress, I'll be living in, so I'm giving up this council house.'

Sandra, barely nineteen, was stunned by this news and felt rather tearful at what she perceived as a second abandonment. But after giving it some thought, she had a possible solution.

'Maybe you can find work for me down there too,' she suggested, although it wasn't that straight forward. For one thing, there was Danny to consider, she didn't want her brother to feel deserted either.

'Danny's chosen to go his own way. He's working now and he'll not mind,' her mother insisted.

Sandra was not so sure. Danny was vulnerable and she wanted to stay in close proximity. Even though she didn't see him that often, she had hoped to stay local, just in case he did need her. It was also going to be hard to leave the family home after all these years. Whilst it had given her some bad memories, it also held many happy ones too.

Thoughts of her missing father were never far away either. She still intended to visit him, hoping that she might persuade him to return to England. Surely the love of his wife and children were a stronger pull than living a single life in Poland.

She desperately needed money to fund such a trip and that finally persuaded her to join her mother down south. She was delighted when she managed to secure work as a waitress, working in another hotel, not far from Maria's. Within two months, with the additional help of generous tips, she had saved up enough cash to pay for both the railway and boat tickets to Poland. Once again she contacted the Fregata travel agency, recalling how helpful they had been with her father's travel arrangements in the past. Also her godfather Seweryn, after hearing of her plans, very kindly stepped in to help.

'I'll arrange for you to stay overnight at a hotel near Liverpool Street Station in London. It will make it much easier for you to catch the train the following morning,' he informed her. 'Please give Kazik my best wishes,' he added, feeling extremely sad about his friend's demise.

Sandra really appreciated this support, making her feel slightly more confident about what she perceived to be quite a daunting journey on her own. She had such mixed feelings about her visit, wondering what state her father would be in, yet she felt she had no choice. She must seek out her father and find out his intentions for the future.

Summer 1969

On her arrival in Poland, instead of travelling straight to Wasilkow, where she knew her father was staying, Sandra arranged to meet up with her Aunt Eugenia and family in Zielona Gora. The usual warm welcome helped her relax and her aunt, an excellent seamstress, made her a generous offer.

'Would you like me to make you a dress Olenka before you set off to Wasilkow? I have this pretty flowered cotton material and I'm sure the blue colour will really suit you.'

Sandra nodded in approval and thanked her politely.

The visit proved beneficial in another way too. As the two cousins became reacquainted, Halina suggested she accompany Sandra on the next stage of her journey and Sandra willingly accepted her kind offer.

The two of them took a train to Bialystok where they had arranged to meet Kazik. Sandra felt increasingly nervous but having Halina's company certainly helped. As they alighted from the rail carriage, Sandra scanned the many faces on the platform. She hesitated for a moment, as a tall, bald man came toward her - he seemed so thin and stooped his face gaunt and lifeless. Was it really her father?

She approached him eagerly and although there was no welcoming hug or any acknowledgment of how pleased he was to see her, he did respond to her warmly.

'How well you look Olenka,' he remarked, smiling weakly.

As Sandra came up close to him, she felt unable to say the same but instead reached out and gently took hold of his arm. It seemed painfully thin. Together, the three of them walked along the streets, eventually arriving at a small wooden house, located by the edge of a river, not far from where his brother Janek lived. Once inside, Kazik showed them his single room, with just a small glass-covered veranda beyond. Sandra looked around the gloomy surroundings and her heart ached. There were few items of furniture and a very limited number of possessions. The air felt damp and chilly and was thick with cigarette smoke.

'Have you been able to find work?' Sandra asked hesitantly.

'Yes, I work shifts, in a local textile factory,' he replied.

She could see her father was struggling and it was unbearable to see him living alone in such poor accommodation. She bit her lip but couldn't hold back her frustration.

'Father,father why have you done this? Why don't you come back with me to England?' she begged.

Kazik shook his head and muttered in Polish, 'People don't like me in England.'

'Well your family like you,' Sandra said tearfully, 'and we want you to come back.'

Kazik didn't respond and simply reverted to small talk.

That evening, he insisted the girls sleep on his mattress whilst he went to lie down in the veranda. It was hard for Sandra to settle as so many dark thoughts filled her mind. Perhaps the best option, she decided, was to enjoy this time with her father, especially if he had no intention of returning home.

Over the next few days, Sandra and Halina explored some of their old haunts where they had played as young children and were especially pleased when Kazik joined them on a fishing expedition in the local river. Sandra decided to capture the scene on her camera, realising it would be something good to share with her mother.

However, during the course of her visit, Sandra became increasingly troubled as she regularly spotted her father holding his stomach, as if gripped by troublesome pain. Because he never mentioned it, Sandra didn't either, fully aware that it would be a closed subject to Kazik.

After a week's stay, she felt great sadness and almost a sense of foreboding, as the time to say goodbye approached.

'I really want to give you presents to take back home ....but I don't get paid until next week,' Kazik explained wistfully. After some hesitation, he came up with an idea, 'What I'll do is try and post them on to you, at Eugenia's house.'

Sandra thanked him in appreciation but she could barely contain her feelings of despondency. How could she even begin to say farewell when she knew this may well be the last time she would ever see him. The reality of that was too hard to contemplate.

As they stood together on the railway platform, she studied her father one last time, taking in a last memory. There was still no final hug between them but she noticed her father's eyes were misting over and she was aware that his body was shaking. When she climbed aboard the train, she stared out of the window until she lost sight of him. Tears flowed and she felt the pain of this parting more than any other. What was to become of him? Had he found true happiness back in his homeland? She doubted it. Had she done enough to persuade him to return? In truth, he had always been strong willed and did what suited him. She must accept his decision, recognising that he was a mentally ill man with many ongoing issues. But how would she relay the news to those who loved him back home?

On their return to Zielona Gora, Sandra decided to discuss the whole issue with her Aunt Eugenia.

'Olenka, I'm sure your father is definitely happier, being back in the country where he truly belongs,' her aunt reassured her.

Sandra listened but it was his overall health that really concerned her.

'Did you take the letter to the doctors that my mother sent you?' she ventured.

Eugenia was flustered, 'I gave it to my neighbour for safe keeping,' she replied.

Sandra found this most puzzling but decided not to press the issue. There seemed no mileage to be gained by getting angry or questioning her further. Besides it wouldn't alter the situation. It was futile to try and persuade her father to return and she felt no doctor would be able to, either.

When her father's parcel arrived later that week, Sandra felt even more troubled – to think he had thought of them and spent money on presents when he had so many needs of his own.

'I want my father to come back,' Sandra cried bitterly as her aunt held her close, not knowing how to respond.

On her journey back to England, Sandra felt weighed down by the reality of the whole situation. As she carried the presents carefully on her lap, she fell into deep thought. Would Maria and Danny be touched to think that he had thought about them or would they be annoyed, thinking presents were no substitute for his presence and didn't make up for their loss. Would they accept that he wasn't going to return and would Danny, in particular, be angry? Or would the whole situation be just like so many others in the past, a problem to be brushed aside and never spoken about?

By the time she arrived back in Manchester, it was late at night and now Sandra had a more pressing matter to deal with. Where was she going to sleep? She'd recently had correspondence from her mother and discovered she'd returned from Eastbourne and was now employed as a manageress at the Albion Hotel, located in the city centre. Sandra looked at her watch and realised it was too late an hour to try and make contact. Feeling increasingly anxious, she turned to two of her fellow travellers, both young girls of similar age, and explained her predicament.

'You are welcome to stay overnight at ours,' they suggested and although they were strangers, Sandra gladly accepted. The following morning, after expressing her appreciation, she left the girls and set out to make contact with her mother by telephoning The Albion.

'Can we meet up at the hotel, later on today?' Sandra asked, when finally the switchboard operator put her through to Maria.

'I'll do my best to arrange that,' her mother replied.

'Can you see if Danny can come and join us too? I have something to give you both,' Sandra explained.

That afternoon, as the three of them sat together in the hotel foyer, all were in sombre mood.

'I have presents for you … from father,' Sandra explained, her voice quivering and full of emotion as she handed over two small parcels, wrapped in brown paper.

As Maria opened her gift to reveal a mirror, she studied it carefully. It was a mirror that had been handmade in Jerusalem; making her wonder if Kazik had purchased it as a reminder of the time he'd spent in Palestine, back in the 1940s. As she caught sight of her reflection, Maria's eyes filled with tears for she saw the face of a woman now alone. She knew deep in her heart that her husband would never return and that this was in effect the end of her marriage. She tried hard to suppress her feelings but she lifted the mirror up close to her chest and sighed deeply. No-one spoke for a while and the silence was deafening.

'I'll open my present now,' Sandra said, trying to deflect the tension.

She opened it carefully, revealing the figure of a bison, carved in wood, with its tusk acting as a paper knife. She slowly ran her fingers along its smooth, shiny surface – vowing that it would always be treasured and permanently displayed in a prominent place in her home, as a constant reminder of her father.

Next, it was Danny's turn. Sandra, feeling rather disgruntled with her brother's recent attitude, almost threw the parcel in his direction.

'He bought you this,' she said, hesitating before adding, 'yet you haven't even bothered to write to him or make contact with your father.'

Danny didn't respond. He simply opened the gift to reveal a travel clock which he seemed happy to keep. Just like his father, he internalised his frustrations and his resentment and wouldn't speak of them. He was a typical eighteen years old, facing all the traumas of becoming an adult. He needed his father's support but it was not there, nor would it ever be again.

Danny left hastily, leaving his mother and sister to chat over their future plans.

'I'm going to have to find somewhere to live, and I'll need to look for work back here, now you've returned to Manchester,' Sandra remarked.

'I'll contact the Hawks and see if they'd be willing to put you up whilst you look for somewhere,' her mother offered, 'Once you find work, you can rent a flat of your own.'

Sandra wasn't sure how easy that would be but she agreed to the suggestion.

As the two of them left the hotel, there was one more issue she was eager to raise with her mother. She wasn't sure if she would want to hear the answer or indeed how her mother would react but she needed to know.

'Mother, I must ask you - do you really want dad to come back?'

Her mother paused for a moment but then she spoke in hushed tones.

'If I'm honest, not really,' she said, 'your father has become an old man now.'

Sandra was sad to hear her response but she understood exactly what her mother meant. She knew her mother had loved Kazik, despite his illness, but over the years his many breakdowns had taken their toll and they really had aged him. He might have been twelve years older than Maria but in recent years this age gap had seemed even greater. Her mother was still attractive and appeared younger than her years. Despite her meagre resources, she had always made the effort to be well -groomed and stay trim and been determined to display a positive, youthful attitude to life. Sandra recognised that her mother had always faced life's problems with fortitude and an irrepressible spirit so would undoubtedly learn to cope with her single status. Sandra studied her mother carefully and it set her thinking.

'Would you like a new partner in time mum?'

Her mother paused then smiled.

'Have you actually met someone already?' Sandra asked on seeing her response.

'Certainly not!' her mother replied emphatically.

'It's just the way you smiled, I thought you might have.'

'No, I don't want a relationship. I've had enough sex to last me a life time!'

And with that they both broke into fits of laughter and parted with a loving hug.

CHAPTER 23
MANCHESTER 1970s

Sandra was now facing a dilemma: an absent father, a mother with a live- in job and a brother who was preoccupied with his own problems. Where was she to go? The Hawks had kindly agreed to let her stay with them but it was only ever intended as a temporary measure and now, after six weeks, she felt it time to move on.

With independence looming, Sandra felt increasingly vulnerable, all too aware of the responsibilities that would come with single living, particularly the financial implications. Fortunately, she was soon successful in gaining employment, working as a clerk for 3M, an American manufacturing company. This meant she could afford rental on a bed sit and soon managed to locate one within a tenement block at Harper Hey, a suburb of Manchester.

The Hawk's son, Robert, offered to take her there, dropping her off outside, with her transistor radio in one hand and a single suitcase in the other. On entering the stark room, Sandra looked around and felt an immediate sense of isolation. Apart from a single bed, a chest of drawers and a small wardrobe, there was little in the way of furnishing and the room seemed so cold and uninviting. As she sat on the edge of the bed, she felt overwhelmed and she certainly wasn't prepared for what was to come. She was a young, attractive girl with a gentle, rather naïve nature and had little knowledge or experience of worldly matters. She trusted people, taking them at face value, and at that moment she longed for somebody, anybody, to befriend her.

Initially, every night, on her return from work, she saw no-one and spent the time alone in her room. Then her loneliness intensified as she began to feel quite ill. Her throat ached, she shivered uncontrollably and her temperature soared. A visit to the doctor revealed she was suffering from an acute case of pharyngitis. She really needed to keep warm but realised that heating cost money. Fortunately the landlord called round to see how she was doing and generously put some coins in the meter but his kind gesture simply compounded Sandra's feeling of homesickness. She decided to make contact with her mother but her response was not at all what Sandra expected.

'I'm really busy, corukna, as I'm moving to London next week.'

'London!' Sandra exclaimed, trying not to cry.

'Yes, I'm going to work in a hotel down there... as a manageress.'

'What! You've only just moved back up here.'

Her mother's inability to settle troubled Sandra and it reignited all the pain and feelings of being 'abandoned', especially as she'd had no fore-warning of this relocation. Still not officially an adult, she hoped for her mother's support but it seemed it wasn't forthcoming. What was happening to her family? Every week it seemed to be further fragmented.

Her loneliness was becoming so unbearable, she mustered up the courage to go downstairs and knock on the door of the flat below. A young blonde-haired girl came to the door and after brief introductions, 'Sheila', a student, invited Sandra inside.

Over the following days, the two girls developed a good friendship and enjoyed evenings out together, often palling along with Sheila's boyfriend, Harry. Harry and Sheila soon decided to live together and moved into a new flat. They were keen for Sandra to pay them a visit.

'Why don't you come over, this weekend,' they suggested. 'We'll have some drinks at our local, and then you can stay over at ours and catch the bus home in the morning.'

Sandra readily accepted, always eager to have company. The next Saturday, it was almost midnight when the three of them arrived back at the couple's flat.

'You sleep with me in the double bed and Harry can go on the sofa in the other room,' Sheila suggested.

This arrangement worked well until, in the early hours, Sandra suddenly awoke to find Harry joining them in bed.

'He's feeling cold,' Sheila explained as Sandra expressed her disquiet. The next thing she knew, Harry was being intimate with his girlfriend. Sandra immediately tried to leave but as she did so, Harry reached out and grabbed her forcibly by the arm, eager to stop her. She could smell the liquor on his breath and felt utterly repulsed.

'It's not just Sheila that loves you, I do as well,' he whispered, trying to justify his actions and encourage her to stay.

Sandra managed to break free but was unsure what to do. Her instinct told her to leave but it was too late an hour to think about going out on the street. Then, without warning, Harry jumped up, stormed out of the room and took his frustration out on the kitchen window. On hearing the sound of breaking glass, the two girls cowered on the bed, until all became quiet. Sandra felt increasingly ill at ease, especially as Sheila made no apology for her boyfriend's behaviour but just went back to sleep.

Time seemed endless as Sandra lay awake, waiting for dawn to break. As soon as possible, she motioned to leave.

'We'll both escort you to the bus stop,' Sheila insisted.

Sandra, not daring to refuse, simply nodded.

'You'll come and see us again, won't you?' Sheila asked as Sandra finally boarded the early morning bus.

'Yes I will,' Sandra promised, wishing to placate them, but in truth she had resolved never to see either of them again.

Slowly, she put the episode behind her and began new friendships with two other fellow residents - Louie, a young Spanish guy and Sally, of similar age to herself. The three of them discussed the idea of finding a larger flat, for them all to share. Thinking this would be the answer to both her limited finances and her loneliness; Sandra agreed to this and rather prematurely, handed in her notice to the landlord.

'I'm sorry we've been turned down for the flat we were after,' Sally informed her, a few days later. Sandra guessed one of them must have had a bad reference but she kept such thoughts to herself, not wishing for any trouble. But she was worried – where did it leave her?

'My mum, Paula, has a rented house so I'll contact her and see if she can put us up temporarily,' Sally suggested.

Paula seemed a kind woman and generously offered the three of them individual rooms, giving Sandra her upstairs bedroom. At first, Sandra thought nothing of the fact that Paula lived with Christine but soon found herself in receipt of some more unwelcome attention.

She was totally shocked one night, when stirring from sleep, she discovered Paula looking down on her. Her initial reaction was that Paula must have accidentally walked into the wrong bedroom but then when Paula bent down, to reveal she was wearing only her underwear and began to lick Sandra's ear, she realised this wasn't the case.

'What **are** you doing?' Sandra asked, very perturbed.

168

'Don't you like being with a woman?' Paula responded.

'Certainly not!' Sandra replied.

'Well you won't know, unless you give it a try.'

Sandra quickly pushed her off. 'If you come near me again, I'll tell your daughter,' she threatened.

Nothing more was said of the incident but Sandra felt increasingly uncomfortable at the constant number of glances Paula was giving her. It quickly dawned on her that all of the fellow residents were women and no doubt more than just flatmates. Rather than say anything negative to Sally about her mother, Sandra simply suggested the two of them find an alternative flat.

Within weeks they had moved to Newton Heath and Sandra began to feel more settled. As her 21st birthday was approaching in August, she was determined to arrange a small party, hoping to further lift her spirits and enable her to meet new people. Her first invite was to Danny and she was pleased when he brought along a gang of his friends .... and his record player. They spent the entire evening gathered round it, listening to the latest pop music. Unlike many of her peers, Sandra wasn't a fan of The Beatles but preferred the Drifters and the soulful sounds of Motown.

Her mother had sent a gift of money for her birthday and along with her regular wage, it had enabled her to feel more financially secure. It was good to be able to pay her way and meet her half contribution to the rent, which she handed over to Sally every month. So it came as a real shock, several weeks later, when the landlord announced they were to be evicted ....for non-payment of rent. It slowly dawned on Sandra that there was only one possible explanation: Sally must have pocketed all the money. This betrayal by her 'friend' was yet another hard blow.

In desperation, she went knocking on the doors of all the local rental properties in the area, hoping to find somewhere else to go. Just two days before the date of her eviction, she moved to a flat in Levenshulme, a suburb of Manchester and felt relieved to be back on her own. But she was totally bemused. Would life ever be straightforward? Was anyone to be trusted?

She had certainly learnt some valuable lessons, even if it had been in a hard way and gradually, with the passing of time, she realised she was becoming much more independent and able to cope with life's challenges. So it came as rather a surprise when a phone call from Maria brought some unexpected news.

'I'm coming back to Manchester and wondered if we can live together?' Maria enquired.

'What! You want us to live together?' Sandra uttered, feeling very irritated. How annoying of her mother to want them to be flatmates now that it suited her. Why should she oblige, when she felt her mother had left her to fend for herself these last two and a half years. She felt justified in feeling angry, especially when she had been through so much yet had had minimum communication or support.

'When were you thinking of coming back?' Sandra asked, trying to hide her deep resentment whilst also wanting to pin her mother down to an agreed time.

'This Saturday.'

'No, that's far too soon. It's already Wednesday, so there's no chance of me finding us a flat to share .... But I will look for somewhere temporary for you,' was all Sandra could promise.

Sandra felt she had no choice but to ask Paula if she could house her mother in one of her bedsits at Newton Heath and she kindly obliged. Sandra decided to make no mention of Paula's life style but Maria's suspicions were aroused as soon as they were introduced.

'You've a good figure for a woman of your age,' Paula remarked, as she looked Maria up and down.

Maria smiled graciously but thought it rather a strange comment to come from a middle- aged woman. Fortunately, within two months, Maria found herself alternative accommodation at a flat nearer to Sandra, in Levenshulme. The whole complex was quite run down but Maria worked hard to make her place spotless though she soon discovered there were drawbacks to living here too. She became convinced there was a ghost in the place. A previous tenant - an old lady - had died in the adjacent premises a short while earlier. Just going down the corridor to collect coal from the cellar unnerved Maria, convinced that she could hear a voice calling her into the deceased's room.

But there was another more pressing issue for Maria to contend with. Poor health continued to trouble her and despite her resilient spirit, she sometimes felt too unwell to attend work. This led to financial struggles, making her reassess the situation- perhaps there was an obvious solution.

'Can we try again Sandra?' she begged, 'Let's look for a flat together.'

Sandra, although still aggrieved by her mother's actions, agreed to look and soon found one she hoped might be suitable in Fallowfield, three miles south of Manchester's city centre. It was a cosy flat but it had disadvantages. With just one bedroom, it meant they would have to share and there was also a communal bathroom, for use by every other tenant.

'But I guess it's affordable,' Sandra remarked, realising there would be benefits for her too.

'And hopefully no ghosts and no lesbians!' Maria quipped.

So they both agreed to give it a try.

The two of them were happy enough for a couple of months but then in the July of 1972, Sandra found a new interest to distract her. She was out with friends in the city's 'Bierkeller', enjoying a 'chicken and chips in a basket' night, when she spotted a young man. He appeared rather worse for wear, after consuming a few too many German beers.

'Don't you think you've had enough!' Sandra chided, half laughing.

Her comment broke the ice and they began a conversation, quickly discovering how easily and naturally they could chat to each other.

He had soon introduced himself as John Spooner, a joiner who lived with his parents in Chapel-en-le-Frith. At twenty–six, he was three years older than Sandra.

Sandra found him attractive, with his very long blonde hair, his friendly smile and his good chat up lines. John too was smitten, especially liking the fact that Sandra seemed quiet, rather than the typical girls he met who never knew when to stop talking! He was soon offering to take her home and both agreed to meet up again.

After several weeks, Sandra was keen to introduce John to her family. She didn't see Danny that often but she was still eager to gain his approval, so she arranged for the three of them to meet.

Danny got on well with John and he could see how smitten the two of them were.

'Let me know when you two get married, I want to be there!' he joked, as they said their goodbyes.

Sandra smiled as she coloured up. She was pleased Danny approved of her choice …but his comments were embarrassing, they weren't even engaged yet.

When John did propose, not long afterwards, she happily agreed and they began to plan a summer wedding for a date in June the following year, marking eleven months since they'd met.

They decided to have the service at the local Catholic church, St Kentigern's, in Fallowfield, followed by an afternoon reception at a nearby hotel. They agreed to invite twenty guests, with Maria and Danny at the top of the list, along with John's parents.

Sandra was keen to share her news with everyone but she failed to realise the impact it would have on her brother. He was still struggling with the absence of his father and now, although barely an adult, he was facing the prospect of life alone. As Sandra was going to be with John, her future certainly didn't include him. As for his mother, it seemed since Kazik had left, she had rediscovered herself and become totally self-sufficient. Where did that leave him? What was **his** future to be? There was nothing to hold him in Manchester but where else could he go?

Over the following days, his life began to go downhill and the bad decisions he made, ultimately had a devastating impact on all of them.

CHAPTER 24
POLAND - 1973

Back in Poland, in recent weeks, Kazik's condition had deteriorated. Not only was he suffering mentally, his physical health was causing him great concern. Although he was still employed in a local factory in Wasilkow, on many occasions he felt just too unwell to go.

Over the last four years, his life had not been easy. He was glad to be living near to his brother Janek but his thoughts often turned to Olenka and Seweryn. Whilst he had no wish to return to England, he missed seeing them and constantly wondered how they and Maria were faring.

He never talked to anyone of his time in the army, having been forbidden to do so, but it still haunted him, thirty years after his release. The sights he'd witnessed, firstly in cattle trucks, then in prison at Star Vileyka and finally in the gulag at Ryazan, although in the distant past, were still vivid in his mind: the inhumanity of the Russian guards towards the pregnant women, the cries of the children as they suffered hunger pangs and the brutal treatment of the sick and disabled. Worse still were the images of sheer horror and terror; men being garrotted, women and even young girls being raped and horror of horrors, babies being thrown against walls. There were the sickening cries he could still hear and the appalling smell of excrement and dead corpses that he could still sense. These flashbacks constantly tormented him.

Kazik appreciated when one of his siblings visited him but they all recognised that he was suffering with his mental health. Aware of Kazik's deteriorating state, Janek would try to call round any evening he could..

'Are you regretting coming back to Poland?' he asked, trying to encourage Kazik to open up. 'Do you want to go back and see your family?' he persisted.

Kazik's response shocked him. 'No! No! I won't ever go back. My wife has found someone else. She won't want me now,' he shouted.

Janek was upset by this revelation but soon realised his brother was suffering delusions and doubted the truth of the remark. Surely Maria would never be unfaithful, especially when she had been loyal to him through so much. He was sure it was in his imagination but he found it immensely sad.

One evening, he was further perturbed when Kazik was nowhere to be seen, yet the fire was blazing away.

'Kazik! Kazik!' he shouted, sure that he must be around somewhere, 'It's only me,' he added reassuringly.

Still there was no response. Suddenly, Janek sensed a movement and realised Kazik was actually hiding behind the fireplace. He was suffering terrible flashbacks, convinced that the NKVD were calling to take him away again. As he came face to face with Janek, he stared at him in terror and wrestled against him, grabbing his younger brother by the arm.

Immediately, Janek recognised that his brother had relapsed so much, he needed urgent medical attention. He called for an ambulance and Kazik was admitted into hospital where he underwent psychiatric help.

After several days, Kazik was released but the stomach pain he had experienced for so long began to escalate and become unbearable. Despite this, he felt compelled to go back to work. At first, he spoke to no one of his agony and as his appetite failed and he became weaker, he still struggled on.

His spirits were temporarily lifted one day when a letter arrived from England, from his beloved Olenka. Recognising her handwriting, he opened it with anticipation. A photograph fell onto his lap. Picking it up, he saw a picture of his daughter with a young man, apparently named John. He stared at it for ages. She had written news that she was to be married; it was hard for him to imagine that his young daughter was now to be a wife but he felt so proud of her.

Over the following days, he studied the photo and restudied it, the young couple looked so happy and he felt pleased that his daughter had chosen well. When Janek called round, he was eager to show him the picture.

'I hope I can meet up with them soon,' Janek remarked, 'maybe I could even persuade them to come and live here.'

'I just hope I live long enough to hear they've got married,' Kazik replied ruefully.

Over the following days, his health continued to decline and he was forced to seek further medical help. It was discovered he had advanced stomach cancer. The doctor offered him strong pain killers but he refused to take them, convinced they were useless. He took to his bed and his sister Renia and Janek regularly called round to look after him. As his pain intensified, he slowly weakened and on the first day of March, 1973, he died, just a month short of his fifty- seventh birthday.

When Janek called in later, on his regular evening visit and found him lifeless on the bed, he was distraught. To think he had been reunited with his brother only to lose him so soon was hard to bear but he also deeply regretted not being with him as he died. His brother had suffered so many trials and much torment under the Russians yet he had been such a hero at Monte Cassino, winning four medals for his bravery. Now, this last courageous act had gone unnoticed.

'I had no idea he was so ill,' his boss remarked when Janek informed him of Kazik's death.

'I guess you didn't know that he was a hero?'

'How do you mean, a hero?'

'Well, his bravery won him several medals in Ander's army during World War Two. He was a member of the 2nd Polish Corps fighting under the command of the British Eighth Army. He took part in the famous battle of Monte Cassino in which the Germans were finally beaten by the Allies, forcing them to withdraw from Italy.'

'I never knew,' his employer muttered, shaking his head and taken aback by this news. 'I had no inkling that such a brave man was working for us. He never spoke of his past or shared either his triumphs or his torments. What a tragedy.'

Back in England, Maria and Sandra were both at home when the telegram arrived. Maria stared at the postmark, ….realising it was from Poland, she held it tightly, for a brief moment, before reading its contents. The bold words were brief but stark:

'Kazik died on March 1st 1973.'   Janek

Immediately, she passed it to Sandra, without saying a word.

For a while, Sandra was unable to talk, even to think. Her father was gone; now she'd never see him or talk to him ever again. Endless questions spun around her head, consuming every waking thought. Why had he left them? Had he actually found the peace he was so desperately seeking? She doubted it, not when he had died alone and in such pain. It was too unbearable to contemplate. Had he thought of her before he died? Did he regret his actions? There were no answers to bring her peace.

Nor was there any discussion with her mother about their loss. Maria seemed to accept his death as inevitable and showed no emotion, not outwardly at least. After much thought, Sandra realised that her mother had done her grieving those many months earlier, when her husband had deserted her.

It was Sandra who finally raised the issue.

'I'm not sure what to do about the funeral; do you think I should go?'

'I don't think you should consider it, what with the expense,' Maria replied but then she made a suggestion.

'I'll ring your god- father Seweryn, he needs to know Kazik has died and I'm sure he'll advise you what is best.'

'He said he doesn't think travelling over there will do any good,' Maria told her daughter a few days later. Whether she had actually contacted Seweryn was in doubt but Sandra decided not to go.

Later that week, an envelope arrived from Janek, containing haunting photographs of her father as he was laid to rest. Sandra glanced at them briefly but then threw them to one side. To look at her father's emaciated, lifeless body in his wooden coffin was too real and far too painful. She certainly didn't want her last memory of him to be so bleak. She would much rather remember her father as that loving man who could show compassion during those times when he felt well.

'You must focus on your wedding my froglet,' Maria said, putting her arm around her daughter, 'you must concentrate now on happier times.'

'Yes but what about Danny? He needs to know that his father is dead.'

'I haven't heard from your brother for quite a while. I'm even unsure where to find him. We will have to hope he contacts us and then we can tell him. I'm sure he will want to be at your wedding.'

Over the next couple of months, Sandra tried to follow her mother's advice and focus on her wedding plans. It was hard to accept that her dad wasn't going to be there and this left her with a dilemma. Who could she ask to give her away? Mr Hawk immediately came to mind and she was grateful when he readily accepted.

Her godfather Seweryn also very kindly offered financial help, providing five hundred pounds as a wedding gift, plus a two hundred pound payment towards Maria's outfit.

On the day of the wedding, as Sandra walked down the aisle of the church, with her arm steadied by Mr Hawk, her eyes scanned the sea of smiling faces of the assembled guests. She was desperately hoping to spot her brother. He hadn't acknowledged her invite but she still hoped it had reached him somehow. But there was no sign of him.

Throughout the ceremony, although Sandra tried hard not to dwell on it, she felt a sense of unease and disappointment. Why hadn't he turned up? Was he unwell? The uncertainty was what made it so difficult.

Maria also felt a certain sadness, despite feeling immensely proud and happy for her beautiful daughter. Her concerns were not just for Danny but also for herself. Now that they were married, John and Sandra were going to live temporarily with John's mother and father in Chapel- en- le- Frith in Derbyshire. This left Maria alone in their flat, meaning she could no longer afford the rent which they had previously shared.

'I'll come and help you look for a new place,' Sandra offered on her return from her honeymoon in Devon.

Together, they went searching for lodgings, focusing in the Fallowfield area, in the suburbs of Manchester. They located a small flat which sounded ideal on paper. On inspection, both of them were shocked by its dirty state, causing Maria to let out a few choice words! Sandra was quite taken aback. In all her years, she had never known her mother to swear. As compensation, the landlord offered to give Maria two weeks rent free and this sealed the deal.

She was equally pleased to find new employment at Portman Garages, as a book keeper, working for a Pakistani family. Her wages were enough to enable her to both pay the rent and have some left over for her daily living expenses. She soon set about making it spotless and seemed quite settled, deciding to get herself a dog to keep her company. She did wonder how she could contact Danny to tell him of her new address but as for her deceased husband, she made no reference to him, to anyone.

Meanwhile, Sandra discovered living with her in- laws wasn't easy. Her mother-in-law was a rather domineering, formidable woman and not a person to be crossed. Within six months, Sandra was pleased when they were able to move out, having decided they could afford to rent a flat in Whaley Bridge. This flat was owned by Mrs Percy Woolley who was a good friend of the artist LS Lowry and although it was not ideal, as it suffered from rising damp, it was 'home' and the two of them could now enjoy being alone together. They were both determined to save up enough money to eventually buy their own house.

Sandra enjoyed married life but thoughts of Danny and his whereabouts were always in the back of her mind. Nor could she forget the pain of losing her father and slowly a plan began to formulate in her mind on how she could keep his memory alive.

CHAPTER 25
WHALEY BRIDGE - 1974

'Why don't we arrange a trip to Poland,' Sandra suggested to John, one evening, 'I'd like you to meet my family and show you all the places that I've talked about.'

'That sounds like a good idea,' he replied, 'I'm happy to make all the travel arrangements, if you tell me where you'd like to go.'

'I'm sure we can stay with Aunt Eugenia in Zielona Gora but I also want you to meet Janek and his family in Wasilkow which is about seven hundred kilometres further north.'

Then Sandra paused, taking a sharp intake of breath, 'Whilst we are there, I'm also keen to visit the cemetery where my father is buried.'

John, realising the importance of this visit, had a thought of his own, 'Let's take my camera with us and take lots of photographs. Then we can share them with your mother on our return.'

On their outward journey, after taking the ferry across the Channel, the two of them caught a train from the Hook of Holland for the long ride to Poznan, a city in west-central Poland. As they travelled through the night, the guards constantly roused them, wishing to examine their transit visas, meaning there was little opportunity for sleep.

'I think we had our documents stamped nine times in all,' John commented wearily to his fellow passengers the following morning.

Later that day, as the train arrived at the German border, between east and west Berlin, it ground to a halt although no passengers were allowed to alight. John noticed the guards scanning underneath the train, using their torches and mirrors but this time he kept his observations to himself. Everyone was relieved when permission was given to move on and continue their journey. However, on their arrival at the Polish border, a customs officer now came on duty and after picking up one of John's three suitcases, he realised one of them felt particularly light. Feeling suspicious, he indicated he wished to see inside. John was eager to comply but to his horror, he discovered it wouldn't open, the key just didn't seem to fit. It took an age but eventually John forced it open, even though it turned out to be the wrong key. When the impatient guard finally surveyed the contents – some simple writing equipment – he tossed it aside dismissively and marched off.

After several hours, Poznan station finally came into view and Sandra was pleased to see her cousin Halina waiting on the platform, ready to escort them on their final train journey to Zielona Gora. This new steam locomotive seemed so slow compared to the previous train and the relatively short journey took almost six hours. Fortunately Sandra and Halina had a lot of catching up to do, including much talk of the wedding, which helped the time to pass. At last, they were at Aunt Eugenia's house.

Sandra proudly introduced her new husband to all the family and he was welcomed by everyone. John felt slightly ill at ease as they all chatted away in Polish but slowly he learnt 'who was who' and even began to master a few useful phrases.

The following morning, Eugenia took Sandra to one side, 'I have something to give you, Olenka,' she said as she handed her a bank book.

'This belongs to you now …. it was your father's but he wanted you to have his money,' she explained.

Sandra accepted it gratefully then, after some consideration, she responded.

'I would really like to spend some of this, on a lasting memorial to my father. I wonder if Janek might be able to help me organise it.'

'I'll get in contact with Janek and arrange a time for us to go to Wasilkow,' Eugenia replied, 'I also wondered if you'd both like to visit Warsaw whilst you are over here.'

Sandra and John willingly accepted this suggestion and enjoyed a visit to the capital later that week. It had largely been rebuilt since the war but John was intrigued to tour around the old town and take pictures of the castle undergoing restoration.

A few days later, John and Sandra journeyed to Wasilkow where they were warmly greeted by Janek and his family. After sharing a lovely meal, they found themselves chatting late into the evening.

'I'll take you to see your father's grave tomorrow,' Janek promised, 'and we can discuss some ideas after that.'

As Sandra stood facing her father's burial plot, the following morning, she struggled to contain her emotions. It seemed so surreal to think she would never see her father again and that he had chosen to spend his later years in such a solitary way. She truly wished he had managed to find some peace during those last months but she knew in reality, without the help of morphine or the support of the medical profession, he must have suffered a tormented end to his life. She turned to John.

'Please take a photo of the grave, although I'm not sure if mother will want to see it.'

'It might upset her,' John agreed, 'but I think we should come back to Poland next year and persuade your mother to join us.'

'It won't be so easy for her,' Sandra replied, knowing her mother's reluctance to revisit anything from the past.

'I guess difficulties might arise when we have to travel by rail through eastern Germany,' John replied, 'but let's see what she says.'

On their return home, Maria was happy to look through the photos, especially responding to pictures of Warsaw. It was the first time Sandra had ever heard her talk about her city of birth.

'I used to go to that shop,' she said, becoming quite animated as she recognised the old market square, 'It's where I bought my stationery for school,' she continued.

Sandra listened with interest but didn't like to question her further on this topic. (It was only much later that Sandra bitterly regretted not using the opportunity to ask her more about her upbringing.) But there was one question she was keen to have answered.

'We were wondering mother if you would like to go with us, the next time we visit Poland. All Kazik's family are keen to meet you and ..'

'I'm not sure,' Maria interrupted, 'I really wouldn't want to visit Warsaw …and what if I'm unwell.'

Sandra understood and decided to give her time to think about it.

Over the following weeks, Maria made a decision to move away from Fallowfield and found herself employment in Normanton in Derbyshire. She had been offered work at a Boarding School with the role of House Mother which meant she could utilise some of her nursing skills, plus it provided live-in accommodation. She decided once again to have a dog for company and chose a lively spaniel that she named Selwyn, after one of the student houses at the school.

She was hoping this would prove to be a good move and mean that at last she could put some of her troubles behind her. She'd recently had medical treatment for a duodenal ulcer and was generally feeling better in herself, although thoughts of Danny were never far away.

After some persuasion, she finally agreed to join John and Sandra on their next holiday to Poland, during the school's long summer break.

Sandra had recently received a photo from Janek, showing her the memorial he had arranged for his brother and she was looking forward to visiting it. John agreed to make all the arrangements and proposed they travel across Europe by car rather than train, remembering their previous, rather unnerving experience with the guards, plus the intolerable slow speed of the Polish trains.

'I'm going to see the doctor before I go,' Maria informed them, 'I'm so nervous, I'm going to ask him for some tablets to settle me. I don't want any flares up from my ulcer.'

Sandra agreed this was a good decision although in the end Maria didn't feel the need to take them.

The initial drive, from Buxton to Dover, passed without incident. The boat trip that followed, taking them across the Channel to the Hook of Holland was equally uneventful, apart from Sandra experiencing her usual bout of sea sickness. None of them were looking forward to the long journey eastwards to Poland, knowing it meant crossing the communist area of Germany.

'Please don't talk to me about anything to do with Germany,' Maria begged as they stopped overnight in a bed and breakfast in Cologne for a much needed rest. Respecting her wishes, Sandra and John endeavoured to keep any conversation light hearted and Maria appeared relatively calm, although she hardly spoke that evening.

However, the following day, when they arrived at the German border, separating east from west, their car was forced to stop, filling Maria with dread. John's vehicle was quite distinctive - a Toyota Corona -coloured bright electric blue - and it appeared to have drawn special attention. Guards approached, ordering the three of them to step outside whilst they searched the car. Maria, feeling extremely intimidated, became almost paralysed with fear as their German conversation echoed in her ears. She fixed her eyes towards the ground, determined to avoid any contact with the men, it was awakening too many painful memories.

John watched as the guards used their torches to scan inside and out, including the boot and underneath the car. He too remained silent as he listened, hoping he might pick up some of their comments. Sandra put her mind to focusing on their surroundings. She was totally shocked to see so many buildings either completely boarded up or with their windows bricked out. This was a place totally ravaged by war and its aftermath.

If they wished to continue their journey, John was informed they must pay a road toll- a sum of fifteen Deutsche Mark. John explained he could only speak English and that he didn't have the correct currency.

As he continued to procrastinate, an urgent voice came from the back of the car. 'Pay him and let's get moving!' Maria demanded.

Eventually, John reluctantly paid three pounds in English coinage and permission was granted to move on and continue their journey. The relief was enormous even though they still faced another eight hours of travel. It was late into the night when they finally reached Zielona Gora, so after brief introductions and a light supper, they were all more than ready to retire to bed.

The following morning, John made sure his first job was to call in at the local police station, knowing all visitors were required to register and give details of their name and purpose of their visit. With all their three cards duly stamped, he could finally relax. Both he and Sandra hoped Maria might do the same and that she would enjoy being amongst Polish people once more. Certainly, Eugenia and her family welcomed her and treated her as family and they were pleased when she was conversing with them easily.

Later that week, all the family travelled by car to Wasilkow to meet up with Janek and his family. He immediately introduced his wife Janina to Maria and the two of them chatted happily. He then offered to take them to see Kazik's grave, with its new memorial, bought with Sandra's donation.

Sandra, although concerned how Maria would react, didn't want to miss this opportunity. As they stood in front of a grey marbled cross, rising four feet into the air and dominated by a large statue of Christ, Maria went very quiet but showed no real emotion. It was Sandra who was overcome with sadness. As she studied the simple black plaque, resting at the base and inscribed with Kazik's full name and his date of birth and death, a terrible sickness came over her, along with a deep sense of unease. Tears welled up and she sobbed quietly for all they had lost.

'I think you two should go again tomorrow but on your own,' John suggested to Sandra later that evening, believing Maria was holding back. His intuition proved correct. On their second visit, Maria wept as she stood alongside her daughter. Although they remained silent, they both knew their grief didn't need any spoken words.

'Let's go on from here and visit my sister Renia in Lidzbark,' Janek suggested later that week. It meant a long five hour journey by car, often on poor quality, cobbled roads but Sandra was especially pleased to think she would be able to catch up with her cousin Julek, Renia's son and introduce him to both her husband and mother for the first time.

The reunion that followed was another opportunity for celebration and everyone appreciated the Polish meal that was served, along with several glasses of vodka. Even Maria who usually kept off the drink, participated. The atmosphere grew ever merrier as the evening progressed.

A fellow guest -a friend of Julek - then offered to entertain them all on his accordion. He began with a rendition of a well-known folk song but it soon became apparent, he was singing in German. Suddenly, in the hushed room, everyone's attention was drawn to Maria. Her relaxed mood had altered. Her face was now transfixed as she stared ahead.

'Please, please, stop singing, I can't bear to hear that tune,' she begged as she cupped her hands over her ears.

She had instantly been transported back to thirty years earlier; despite the passing of time, the memory was as vivid as ever. She was now that fourteen year old girl being forced to march to work by her German guards, having to sing songs over and over, with words that resounded in her head.

The young man fell silent, truly upset that he had offended one of his host's special guests. It took a while for Maria to compose herself but everyone tried to carry on as normal. Sandra was deeply moved – this was one of only a few occasions that she had seen her mother so distraught, it was so rare for her to drop her guard. It was a stark reminder of just how much she had held back and for Sandra, it was another moment she would never forget.

Once again, she would have liked to have asked Maria more but decided she better not- for she had no wish to upset her further.

Later on, during their stay at Renia's, Maria surprised everyone by making a second reference to her younger days, but this time she was more open and happy to share her memory.

All the family had decided to visit one of the beautiful lakes near to Lidzbark and enjoy the warm weather. The women all decided to dress appropriately and put on their swimming costumes.

'Do you fancy going for a dip?' Sandra asked her mother, as some of the group ventured into the water.

Immediately, Maria vehemently shook her head, 'No, I'm really not keen… actually I nearly drowned once, as a young girl, I was swimming in the River Wisla, near my home in Warsaw when I had to be rescued …… it put me off water for life!'

This was the first time Sandra had realised her mother had such an aversion but she made light of it and simply accepted Maria's decision to stay on dry land and enjoy a smoke.

The rest of the holiday proved less eventful and on departure day, Maria expressed her appreciation at spending such a lovely time getting to know Kazik's extended family.

'Thank you so much,' Maria enthused as she said her final goodbyes. Everyone hugged her and made her promise to return one day.

Initially, there had been one or two family members who had showed a certain reticence toward her, thinking that Kazik had left her because she had found another man but most of the family recognised this was totally untrue. They knew when Kazik had mentioned it, he was suffering from paranoia and this was one of his false delusions.

'I'd really like to come back,' Maria assured them but underlying her response was a deep yet silent sadness.

How she longed for a reunion with her son Danny and how she wished that one day he might be able to accompany her to Poland and finally meet up again with his father's family. But would it ever happen? Indeed would she ever see him again? For where, oh where was he?

CHAPTER 26
DERBYSHIRE – 1976/ 77

In the Spring, Sandra and John were delighted to discover she was expecting a baby. Excited at the prospect of being a grand –mother, Maria was now desperate to find accommodation nearer to her daughter and son- in- law in Derbyshire. There was however, one downside to this move; it would mean yet another change of employment.

Once again she was fortunate and managed to be taken on as a purchase ledger at Ferodo, a brake company based in Chapel-en-le Frith, a small town in the north of the county. She also sourced a private room within a lady's house although, within days, realised it was a bad decision. The owner was far too inquisitive and gave Maria no privacy. Even a visit to the communal toilet was seen by the woman as an opportunity to chat. Would she never stop? Maria had always been a woman who enjoyed peace and quiet, so finding the situation infuriating, she set out to find alternative accommodation. It would involve yet another move but it came as a relief when she relocated to 2, Palace Mansions in Marlborough Road, Buxton. It seemed ideal, for her flat was housed within an attractive building with a grey stone façade and had a bright interior. This, she decided, must be more permanent.

She was truly delighted, when just two days before Christmas, she became a grandmother. 'Colette Patricia Spooner' was born at Stepping Hill Hospital in Stockport, weighing in at a healthy 7lbs 12oz. It was a special moment for the whole family. The only tinge of sadness was that neither Grandad Kazik nor Uncle Danny were around to enjoy the arrival of this beautiful baby.

Over the coming days, both John and Sandra realised their small flat in Whaley Bridge was not at all suitable for bringing up Colette; it was not just the lack of space that was a problem, the rooms were continuously damp. After a short search, they managed to find a pretty two- bedroomed cottage in Chapel-en-le Frith that was up for sale. It was located in a conservation area, with a cobbled road outside and a small rear garden. The inside though was rather run down and in great need of an update. For John, with his many DIY skills, this was an ideal project. After securing the purchase, they delayed moving in, whilst he set about gutting it from top to bottom, with the help of a grant. Although working as a joiner at the time for Ferodo, John used every spare moment to work on it – after six months he'd installed a new roof, staircase and bathroom and replaced all the windows and doors. It was finally ready.

Meanwhile, Maria had decided to take up an offer of new employment, working at St Elphin's – a private boarding school for girls – primarily for the daughters of clergy belonging to the Church of England. It was based at Darley Dale, near Matlock.

'Are you enjoying your new job?' Sandra enquired on their next visit, wondering why she had sought yet another new position. The fact that her mother never seemed able to settle anywhere for very long, really puzzled her.

She was certainly not expecting the reply she received.

'I'm actually teaching the girls how to speak Russian!'

Sandra smiled but said nothing. She was proud of her mother for her bilingual talents but she wondered what her father would have thought of his wife teaching Russian to the English and in a Protestant school too.

Maria soon discovered she loved teaching but once again problems with her health began to trouble her. She constantly suffered from stomach cramps and felt distinctively unwell. As usual, she put any concerns to the back of her mind, especially now she had a new granddaughter to focus on. She doted on Colette, always feeling a flood of intense emotion whenever she held her. She had to work hard to hold back tears as she thought of Kazik and everything he had lost – he would never know of or enjoy his beautiful first grandchild. She thought back to the time when she had given birth herself. Even then, she recalled, after Sandra's arrival her husband had missed out, due to his ongoing mental health problems.

She had never shared the full extent of her torment with Sandra and doubted if she ever would. The times when Kazik had threatened her during her pregnancy and even worse ...they were painful memories and she had always felt it best to keep such things to herself. But then he had been an ill man so there were possible justifications for his behaviour.

Now, when she held the baby, she wondered what Colette's own future would hold. The cruel times that she and Kazik and their families had endured in the labour camps would surely never be experienced by any children of today's generation and hopefully any future ones. Colette would no doubt learn one day of the atrocities carried out by the Russians and the Nazis against the Polish race but she wouldn't learn about them from her grandmother. Maria wanted her to be happy and successful, rather than influenced by a legacy of hate or negativity.

She recognised in both Kazik's and her own life, how much their past experiences had affected them. Maybe they had never spoken aloud of their suffering but she was sure that incarceration had been largely responsible for Kazik's dark moods and his paranoia. It had certainly caused many of her own health issues, perhaps even including the latest problems with her stomach.

All her present worries over Danny didn't help either. At least, when Kazik had deserted her, she knew where he had gone but with her son, she had no clue to his whereabouts. This reignited many sad and silent memories of her own father and the fact that she had never discovered what had happened to him either.

She assumed Danny was still living in Manchester but no-one had spoken of seeing him and she'd had no communication with him for over three years. Different scenarios often played out in her head - even the worst one had to be faced - though she wouldn't allow herself to be so negative as to believe it.

To think that her son was now an uncle but had no knowledge of it, made the pain of his disappearance even harder to bear. How Maria wished she knew how to contact him. Turning to Sandra one evening, she spoke her thoughts out loud, as she cradled the slumbering baby.

'If only Danny was around. He'd be so excited to meet his niece. Where do you think he is Sandra?'

'I honestly don't know,' she replied. 'I just hope he's happy, wherever he is … but yes, wouldn't it be good just to know that he's safe and well.'

'Is there any way we can try and trace him?' Maria asked.

She'd never confided her deepest fears to Sandra, particularly her concern that Danny might have inherited some of his father's traits. In those last few months before he disappeared, he had become so withdrawn and sullen. Maybe his erratic behaviour, which at the time she had attributed to normal teenage angst, had been the first sign that he was not well. She recognised Kazik had put immense pressure on his son to achieve and when he failed, in his father's eyes, it had caused Danny such frustration and stress. His rebellion was understandable but his disappearance was another matter. If indeed Danny was struggling, surely now was the time he needed his family the most.

Maria was desperate that they should find him. She could even face the possibility that he might not wish to return home but she really needed to know he was safe –that would be such a great comfort. But where to begin?

'Perhaps … perhaps we could contact the Salvation Army. I believe they can help you trace missing people,' Sandra suggested.

'Yes, that's a really good idea. Can you write to them as soon as possible? 'she begged, 'I will happily give them a donation.'

Just at that moment, Colette woke up.

'You'd just love to meet your Uncle Danny, wouldn't you, my froglet' Maria whispered, as she smiled and cooed at the face beaming up at her.

'I'll write tonight,' Sandra replied.

It was many weeks before a reply came back. Sandra opened the brown envelope, stamped with the Salvation Army logo, with great anticipation:

'It is with regret that we wish to inform you, we have been unable to track down Daniel Szwabowicz …'

Sandra scanned the words and sighed deeply, her disappointment was intense.

'I don't know where we go from here,' she explained to her mother, 'it's so disappointing to have our hopes raised ….only for them to be dashed.'

John, keen to deflect their sadness, had a suggestion.

'Why don't we go to Poland and introduce Colette to all her extended family over there. Maria, you must come with us, they would love to see you again.'

Maria, to their surprise, agreed at once. On this occasion, with Colette being just a toddler, John suggested they choose the quickest form of travel and fly from Manchester to Warsaw.

At Warsaw airport, they found themselves greeted by Janek who was thinking they were staying with him. This presented them with a slight problem as they had actually arranged to go to Aunt Eugenia's house in Zielona Gora. John decided he couldn't expect Janek to take him, so he ordered a taxi, despite the long distance.

The taxi driver was friendly and he seemed to take a liking to Maria. He asked her all about her childhood and for once Maria responded, giving him details of where she had lived as a child.

'Why don't you come back to stay over here?' he asked with a glint in his eyes but Maria simply smiled.

Sitting in the back, Sandra overheard snippets of the conversation but it was only in the future that once again she regretted not listening more carefully.

The holiday did them all good but Maria continued to struggle with ill health, plagued with dizzy spells and unexplained pain. Despite her troubles, she decided she needed to move and find some cheaper accommodation. She eventually found a rented room in Hardwick Square in Buxton and had just begun to settle when in September, 1982, Sandra had some unexpected news.

'John has been offered a job with Hull City Council, as a clerk of works within the City Architect's Department… we are looking for a place to live in the city.'

Maria considered her options. Realistically, she couldn't really afford to move again but the thought of being so distant from her family was unbearable. What was she to do?

Chatting to her landlady about her predicament, she was stunned by her response.

'I'm willing to lend you three thousand pounds, if that would help.'

Maria, after some hesitation, reluctantly accepted her extremely generous offer and used the money to buy a small, terraced house down Exchange Street, off Beverley Road, located near Hull city centre. They all agreed that John would go and stay with her as soon as he started work. Sandra realised she would have to stay with Colette in Chapel-en- le -Frith, whilst they put their house on the market.

By early 1983 the house sold, leaving John and Sandra free to look for accommodation in Hull. Initially, the council offered them a house on the Bransholme estate, north east of the city.

'This will only be temporary,' John assured her, 'hopefully we'll be able to find a house of our own soon.'

Within months, his words became a reality as they acquired a three -bedroomed town house in Telford Street, again in the east of the city. Sandra was happy to be settled and was surprised to discover one of her neighbours was Polish.

Meanwhile, Maria was especially delighted when the City Council awarded her a grant to carry out renovations on her property. At last, she felt settled in a place which could truly be called home. She even began a small clairvoyance business, reading tarot cards under the alias 'Mrs Smith', to earn a little income, in order to repay her debts to her former landlady. Best of all, she loved all the   time she could   spend   with her granddaughter, determined that as Colette   grew up, she would teach her how to cook Polish meals, especially her favourite dish 'pierogi' which she recalled had been one of her husband's favourites too.

Talk of Danny and his whereabouts became a re-occurring topic of conversation within the family. As several years had lapsed since their last search, Sandra suggested they try again.

'I'm going to write to the Salvation Army Missing Persons' Bureau once more. If I send a generous donation they might be willing to have another go at locating him.'

Maria was more than happy to try this. She was so aware that her health was deteriorating and she was desperate for some answers. She still held an intense sadness that she had never discovered what had happened to her own father. She guessed he had died at the hands of the NAZIS - but she would never be sure. To think there was a possibility that she could die without finding her son either, was unbearable.

A few weeks later, Maria suffered an unexplained epileptic fit whilst working with a client and was subsequently admitted into Beverley Westwood Cottage Hospital. The diagnosis was not good.

'I'm sorry to tell you but your mother has a brain tumour,' the consultant explained, 'although it's quite large, there is available surgery but it only has a fifty- fifty survival rate.'

Despite these odds, Sandra and John agreed that an operation was her only real option.

The following days were really tense – had they made the right decision? But then what choice did they have? The operation was scheduled for August. During it, Maria's heart stopped but fortunately the surgeon managed to resuscitate her, although it left her seriously ill. The doctors, concerned that her situation could deteriorate, had to give Sandra some tough advice, 'its best that you sit by the phone for the next three days,' they suggested.

Despite their fears, Maria, with her typical grit, managed to gradually recover but it was obvious she needed time to convalesce, despite her eagerness to return home. She was also now confined to a wheel chair, the operation having left her paralysed on one side. A vacancy was found at a nursing home in Withernsea, a seaside town on the east coast, with the promise that it was only to be a temporary arrangement. After a period of recuperation, Maria went home for a while but by November it became obvious that she was deteriorating. She had lost her appetite and was losing weight so Sandra and John suggested that she stay with them. Unfortunately, by December, the consultant's news was even worse - the cancer had spread to her lungs.

'Sandra, I'm ready to die, I've had a hard life. I was married to an ill man and I've had enough,' Maria said stoically, trying to console her family.

This news weighed heavily on Sandra. It was so unfair. Her mother was only in her fifties and they were not ready to lose her yet. Then unexpectedly, there was a ray of hope concerning Danny - a letter finally arrived from the Salvation Army - might it contain good news which would be just the pick- up her mother needed? Sandra fumbled over the envelope as she felt a surge of hope. The words stared out at her.. they hadn't been able to find any trace of Danny. This was not what Sandra wanted to hear. How could she tell her mother? Perhaps, she decided, the best course of action would be to say nothing. At least that would leave her with hope.

Maria struggled on but a bout of pneumonia weakened her further. She was taken to Castle Hill Hospital and offered chemotherapy but in the end, she refused it. She returned to Sandra's house and for the next fortnight they cared for her day and night. Realising the end was near, on July 12th, a priest came to give her the last rites, followed by a hospice nurse who administered a morphine injection to relieve her suffering. She could battle no more and on the Sunday afternoon of the 13th, in 1986, she took her last breath. She was only fifty-eight.

On hearing of her death, nine year old Colette screamed. She had lost her grandmother whom she truly adored. They were all so numb with grief, no words seemed adequate to comfort each other.

. Sandra chose to have her laid to rest in the city's Eastern Cemetery, following a small service of mass at The Sacred Heart Church in Southcoates Lane, Hull.

Over the following months, Sandra was tormented by the unfairness of her mother's tragic life- recalling how she'd been torn away from her father as a teenager, forced to watch as her mother died of starvation under the Nazis, then living with a mentally ill husband only to be deserted by him and dying prematurely, without seeing her precious son Danny for over fifteen years.

Such dark thoughts constantly plagued Sandra and despite the passing of time, she found it increasingly difficult to come to terms with her loss. After several difficult years, she made two very significant decisions, hoping to finally bring her some closure. Firstly, she sought help from Cruse, a bereavement counselling service and then she set out, utterly determined to discover what had happened to Danny. He needed to know that both his mother and father were now deceased but more importantly Sandra wanted to reassure him just how important he was to her and that he always had been. But where to find him or indeed where to begin to look, was a most daunting prospect ....

CHAPTER 27
HULL 1990s

It was now 1995 and over two decades had passed since Sandra had last seen Danny - a day she remembered only too well- when he had assured his sister, he would be at her wedding but then he'd failed to show. Now she was determined to track him down. She accepted the awful possibility that he might have come to some harm but even that scenario would surely be better than never knowing the truth.

Her first thought was to journey to Manchester, his last known location and try the archive office in the City Central Library. If she could trawl through all the relevant phone books, she may just find him listed.

It turned out to be an overwhelming task, taking several hours but disappointingly, there was not one single entry, under the surname Szwabowicz. Thinking he may not have had any access to a telephone, Sandra now turned her attention to the electoral registers. Even though she had no idea of his address, she felt it worth a punt. Over the next two days, using micro- fiches, she looked at every street in the city for his name... but again without success.

Knowing her brother had had a flat in the Stockport area, during the early seventies, Sandra then decided to visit their local library to repeat the same line of enquiry. After another extremely long process, his name was still not found.

Where next? Sandra began to wonder if Danny might have travelled further up north, even back to Scotland. After consideration, she felt this unlikely, as he had only been a baby when his parents had left Edinburgh in the early fifties. If he had made any contact with her godfather Seweryn in Dumfries, she felt sure Seweryn would have informed the family immediately. Perhaps her only option was to look through every electoral roll in the entire country but it seemed a huge, almost impossible challenge.

Sandra returned to Hull feeling very despondent. Perhaps she should give up on her search and concentrate on other issues.

Meeting up with a friend, she shared the full extent of her desperation to find Danny.

'You know every time I watch television, I search for Danny's face on the screen. I know it sounds absurd but I have so few leads,' Sandra explained, her voice full of emotion.

The friend reached out sympathetically, offering her comfort but then, as an after- thought, she had a suggestion to make.

'Have you ever thought of contacting the census office, maybe their records could help your search?'

Thinking this might be a good idea; Sandra soon formulated a letter, explaining Danny's disappearance and sent it off to their headquarters.

A reply came fairly promptly. Her letter had been passed to the relevant department and they were willing to try and locate Danny's possible address. Sandra would need to send a letter, in a sealed envelope,   in case they were able to locate him, which would then be forwarded to Danny.

With this in mind, Sandra sat and composed a letter. But how could she begin to convey all the emotions of the past twenty years with everything that had happened? In the end, she decided to keep it brief and simply tell him how good it would be to meet him again and include a few family photographs.

After a long, anxious wait, an envelope finally arrived. Nervously she opened it. It was bad news. They explained they had sent her letter off to Danny but it had neither been acknowledged nor returned so there was nothing more they could do.

Whilst a huge disappointment, Sandra reflected ..... did this mean they had been able to locate an address for Danny? She could understand why he may not have wanted to reply but surely this indicated he could still be alive.... a thought which gave her great encouragement.

Sandra discussed the problem with John. Should she give up on her search? Could she cope with further failure and disappointment? Yet, despite these reservations, she knew and John agreed, there was only one real choice – she must persist. It wasn't necessarily that Danny didn't want to see her, she concluded, he might be struggling with ill health or was he too embarrassed to reply? She would never know unless she could find him. But where to go next? She carefully considered her options....

Perhaps, if he was still alive, he might just have a phone in his house and that would mean she could look for a number ...so the following day, Sandra went to Hull Central Library and asked to see every telephone book for the whole of the country. They pointed her to the right shelf which was full to capacity. This was going to be another time consuming job!

On close inspection, she realised the first books, places beginning with the letter A-B, were missing as someone else was looking at them. Instead, she decided to begin her search on the last books, those beginning with Y and Z.

Time after disappointing time, she returned to the shelf to collect the next book, scanning every surname beginning with the letter S, hoping to see D Szwabowicz. By the time she took the last directory back, she had been so long, the A-B one had been returned to the shelf. Disheartened and resigned to failure, Sandra was realising this had been a waste of time… but felt she might as well complete the task.

She turned to the 'S page' for the last time and scanned down. She looked disbelieving at what was in front of her. There was a D **Szwabowicz** and of course, not just a name, an address and phone number too. Could this be her brother and if it was, he was now living where? In Brighton!

With a mixture of excitement and uncertainty, she wrote down the details. She rushed home, anxious to relay her news to John but equally desperate to try the number. Shaking with nerves, Sandra picked up the phone and carefully dialled.

A voice on the other end responded by repeating the number.

'Hello is that Daniel Szwabowicz?'

'Yes, I'm Danny,' he replied rather warily, appearing not to recognise his sister. She was fairly certain it was him but needed confirmation.

'Did you used to live at 105 Finningley Road, Manchester?'

'Yes, I did.'

'Well, it's your sister Sandra speaking to you.'

Danny gasped, totally taken aback and for a moment he didn't know what to say.

Sandra was equally tongue-tied and stumbled over her words, 'I've been looking for you for so long Danny …. At last I've finally made contact….. How are you?'

'I'm a father now,' he replied –'I have a baby son Alex. Actually I have two children - for David is my step -son.'

'That's wonderful!' Sandra enthused, 'whereas I have a daughter, Colette.'

Then came the question Sandra hardly dare ask.

'Did you receive any letters from different organisations, informing you of my attempts to track you down?'

'Yes I seem to think one came fairly recently,' he admitted.

'Why did you never reply?'

'I was nervous, nervous that you might be angry at me.'

Sandra quickly reassured him that she wasn't. She was surprised that he didn't enquire after their parents but then he didn't seem to want to be forthcoming on any topic. So as gently as she could, Sandra explained that both his mother and father were now deceased but spared him any details. She was anxious not to upset him, fearing he might not want to maintain any contact in the future. Again his response was muted. Rather than being upset or angry, he simply made no comment. Sandra was surprised but decided not to pursue it at that moment. Instead, she had one more pertinent question she was eager to ask, although again she was fearful of his reaction.

Rather tentatively, she suggested, 'Would it be alright if I travelled down to see you?'

The line went quiet for what seemed an age but then Danny replied with a simple, 'Yes that would be ok.'

Over the next few days, Sandra made arrangements to travel alone by coach to Brighton and arranged to meet Danny at the main bus station. The anticipation was immense. As she approached the town, her stomach felt in knots. She'd waited twenty-four years for this moment. Would it be the wonderful reunion that she had longed for – the one she'd played out so many times in her head? Would she recognise her 'little brother' and would there be that instant bond again?

CHAPTER 28
BRIGHTON 1995 – HULL 2018

As Sandra alighted from the coach, she began to scan the many faces in the crowded bus station. Surely Danny would be easy to notice because just like his father, he was tall and he'd always dwarfed her. She hoped too that Danny would instantly recognise her, despite the passing of time.

Suddenly she spotted a figure in the distance, leaning against some railings. She was taken aback. Could this stooped man in rather ragged clothes really be her younger brother? He appeared to be unwell and it would be easy to mistake him for a man much older than his forty -four years. His hair was long and tousled whilst his face appeared lined and unshaven... he could, Sandra thought, almost be mistaken for a tramp.

She smiled as she approached him, hoping he wouldn't be able to read her despairing thoughts. She almost tripped as she went to hug him. He responded warmly but as she looked into his deep blue eyes she noticed there was no sparkle. His breath was heavy with alcohol and as he spoke, she noticed all his front teeth were missing.

Sandra grabbed his hand.

'Danny! Danny!' she whispered, too overcome to speak.

'I'm cold,' Danny remarked rather impatiently, 'I've been stood waiting for you for quite a while. Let's go to the pub for a drink.'

Although it wasn't the welcome she had hoped for, Sandra willingly agreed to his suggestion.

'It's so wonderful to see you Danny,' Sandra said, her voice faltering. 'I never thought this day would come. But we never gave up looking for you, you know.'

'You've found me now sis,' he replied, 'and you must come and meet my family.'

Sandra quickly realised he wasn't at all keen to talk about the reasons behind his disappearance, so she avoided any probing questions.

Together, they walked down several streets until finally he stopped outside a block of flats in Vernon Terrace, located in the suburb of Montpelier.

'This is where we live... but don't expect a lot,' he explained rather awkwardly.

After several flights of stairs, they walked into a small flat. As Sandra looked around, she was even more shocked. but tried hard not to show her feelings, especially to Christine, who he introduced as his wife.

She responded with a friendly welcome and was soon offering her toddler Alex for Sandra to hold.

'How old is he?' Sandra enquired, as she cuddled him.

'He's just two,' Christine responded, 'I think he's going to be tall like his dad.'

Sandra felt a great love for her nephew but inwardly she was quite concerned. He looked well cared for but it was his poor living arrangements that troubled her. There were a couple of bare mattresses, laid on the room floor, with little in the way of bedding. It soon became apparent that the couple had no bed.

Sandra studied the two of them in their threadbare clothes and concluded they were destitute. The following day, this was further reinforced when Danny appeared in his wedding suit and explained that it was about the only decent item of clothing that he possessed. On suggesting they take a walk in the local park, he went to put on Christine's anorak.

Sandra guessed that he must be out of work but she was still reluctant to pester him with a barrage of questions and told herself to bide her time. They simply made small talk as he showed her a few of the local sights and neither of them broached the past.

Later that day, they had a simple meal together and afterwards Sandra helped Danny wash the pots whilst Christine saw to Alex's needs. Their conversation was fairly mundane but Sandra couldn't help notice how much Danny's hands were shaking. Aware that she was watching him, he quickly placed his hands deeper into the washing up bowl.

Sandra realised something was wrong and decided the best policy was to question Christine rather than upset Danny. She had taken to Christine and found her open and friendly. Would she be able to fill her in, on Danny's missing years?

Slowly, Sandra built up a picture, although it was all rather hazy as Christine wasn't sure herself just how Danny had got by; she understood that he'd spent his early twenties in Manchester and that initially he'd been employed as a refuse collector. Apparently, he'd soon tired of the work and so had promptly handed in his notice. Next, he'd secured a job at Tesco, where his bosses had been so impressed with his ability, they'd offered him training for a managerial post, however Danny had declined this opportunity. Christine felt he just hadn't wanted the responsibility. Instead, he'd begun odd jobbing in order to pay his way but then, on a whim, he'd made up his mind to visit the south coast. After arriving and liking what he saw, he'd decided to stay and found a waiter's job, working in one of the many seaside hotels. But with no lodgings, he had been forced to make a difficult choice. He ended up living in a cave. Eventually, he'd settled in Brighton and that's where Christine had met him.

'So is he still working in a hotel?' Sandra wanted to know.

Christine shook her head and sighed, 'No, No! He's unemployed at present…. but he tries to survive by odd jobbing. He does have many practical skills,' she added, trying to focus on the positive.

Sandra was eager to know what Danny had told her about his family when they'd first met.

'As far as I can remember, he told me both his parents were dead and although he said he had an older sister, he had no idea of your whereabouts.'

'Actually, his mother died more recently, in 1986,' Sandra replied.

'Oh, that's sad,' Christine responded but she was anxious to reassure Sandra, 'You know he never forgot his Polish roots or his early childhood spent with you.'

She went on to recall a story relating to Danny, which she said typified his love of Polish food. 'One day, at the hotel kitchen where he was working, he'd watched the chef mash a large pan of potatoes and suggested that he add some raw egg. Apparently, according to Danny, it made them taste extra good,' Christine explained.

Sandra smiled, 'Yes, that's just what our mother always liked to do.'

With that, Danny walked in and hearing them talk of Polish food, stirred up an old memory for him. 'Do you remember Sandra, mother making those wonderful cakes in a tin?' he asked.

'Yes and do you remember that pig's head dad cooked once……' And so the conversation went on, well into the night.

The next day, the banter continued but it slowly became evident that despite the arrival of baby Alex, her brother's six year marriage wasn't going well. Christine confided that Danny had been spending all of the little money that was coming in, on drink.

'Do you mean he has a problem?' Sandra asked anxiously.

'Yes, I'm sorry to say, Danny has become totally dependent on drink to get him through each day.'

The realisation that Danny was an alcoholic came as a great shock to Sandra and to see her brother, whom she considered such a clever, good looking man, so downtrodden, really upset her. Like most people with a drink problem, it was clear that he couldn't live with the way he was drinking but he couldn't live without it either.

Sandra returned home with a heavy heart. On her arrival back in Hull, she couldn't contain her emotions any longer and on seeing John, she burst into tears. She shared everything as he listened sympathetically.

'What did he say, when you told him how his parents had died, particularly his father?' John was eager to know.

'Nothing,' replied Sandra, 'he just wouldn't talk about those missing years.'

'Perhaps,' John remarked, 'it was too painful to think about them and all that he has missed …'

'Yes, maybe, but I think he'd taken badly to the way our dad used to treat him, especially when he was a teenager. Dad idolised him at first but then he felt Danny had let him down and it put Danny under so much pressure. It seems Danny has used drink to drown out all those bad memories.'

Over the following days, Sandra couldn't get Danny out of her mind and was eager to help in any way she could. She decided it would be a lovely idea to invite him, along with his family, to come up to Hull for Christmas.

'John will come to fetch you in his car and take you home afterwards,' she explained when they next made contact and she was delighted when he accepted.

The few days of celebration went smoothly and they all relaxed, enjoying all the Polish food and festivities. It felt wonderful for Sandra to be back with her sibling, it had been twenty- six years since she'd celebrated with him and she truly hoped he felt the same. There were so many puzzling questions but she knew she mustn't push Danny for answers. Her ultimate fear was that he'd back off and not wish to see her anymore, so nothing was mentioned regarding his disappearance.

'You'll all have to come back in the summer,' Sandra suggested as they said their goodbyes. 'We can go up to Flamborough and Bridlington and you can see how our seaside compares to Brighton.'

'We'd like that,' Danny replied, promising to return.

The full extent of Danny's money problems had become increasingly apparent to Sandra, so after they left, she decided to put her knitting hobby to good use and make him a sweater. She chose some beige/brown flecked wool and selected a pattern, reminding herself that it would need adjustments; with his height and long arms, the body and sleeves would definitely need extending.

With the jumper complete, Sandra rang Danny and arranged to travel down to Brighton. He seemed pleased with his new sweater and immediately put it on. She also took the opportunity to take Christine to one side, as she was eager to chat in more depth about Danny's drink problem.

Christine slowly explained that he'd had his problems even when they first met, seven years previously. Ironically, they'd met in the pub. She was a local girl, just two years older than Danny, with a young son, at the time. They'd had an instant connection and had soon started living together and married in 1989. Four years later, they'd had Alex who was much loved by them both. But over time things had become increasingly difficult, as Danny became ever more reliant on drink. Yet, she explained, frustratingly, he seemed almost in denial or was it more that he felt powerless to change. There was no doubt he liked his drink; feeling drink didn't judge him or have any expectations of him. It had almost become his friend and his crutch.

'I can imagine,' Sandra suggested, 'there are things from his past he might be trying to forget. Perhaps he's fearful that if he does try to stop, all his anxious feelings will return. But it must be really hard for you, the way he has chosen to live.'

'You're right,' Christine confided, 'I'm seriously considering whether to leave him. I've had enough Sandra; I just can't live like this anymore.'

Sandra completely understood but it left her with a heavy heart. She was desperate to do something, anything to help. On her return home, she discussed the whole issue with John although both agreed it was complex and living so far apart added to the problem.

They had recently sold their house in Telford Street and were now living in a three bed semi-detached house on the eastern edge of the city, down Ridgestone Avenue, in the suburb of Bilton. They were increasingly busy with Sophia, their much loved granddaughter who had arrived in the September of 1996. Despite their commitments to help Colette with child care, Sandra was keen to revisit Poland and this gave her an idea.

'We are going to spend some time in Poland visiting relatives and we were wondering if you would like to join us,' she suggested when she next spoke to Danny. 'I would love you to meet all your Polish family again and they are eager to see you.'

Danny surprised Sandra when he readily accepted but he expressed doubts as to whether Christine would want to join them. In 1997, John, Sandra and Danny journeyed by car to Poland, staying with Wiesiek, Janek's son, and his wife, Krystyna. As ever, the warmth of their welcome enabled Danny to relax and he seemed to enjoy visiting his numerous aunts, uncles and cousins in their various locations. On seeing him again after so many years, Aunt Eugenia was quite shocked at his appearance, especially with his tousled hair and large beard.

'He looks as if he has had a hard life,' she commented. Fortunately, with her speaking in Polish, Danny hadn't understood her remark and for that Sandra was grateful.

In the evenings, he certainly enjoyed a glass or two of vodka and now it was Wiesiek who observed how much vodka Danny could put away.

During their stay, John suggested they all visit the cemetery as Sandra was keen to show Danny his father's headstone. Again Sandra was anxious as to how Danny would react. She watched as her brother stared at the monument for a moment or two then simply said, 'He was a hard bastard!'

On her return home, Sandra mulled over those harsh words her brother had uttered at the grave side. She could understood why he felt so angry, remembering how their father had pushed him so hard to succeed at his studies. She could still remember the beating he had received at the hands of Kazik, after he had received a bad school report. She hadn't witnessed it but she remembered the cries of anguish that had come from his bedroom as he was belted. Sandra had been sitting downstairs with her mother at the time. She recalled her surprise that her mother hadn't intervened but had chosen to say and do nothing. Sandra guessed she was frightened of her husband's reaction if she had tried to stop him. Sandra couldn't help but wonder if this had been the beginning of Danny's troubles. Who was to say?

Sandra also recognised there were other traumatic events from their childhood which had been glossed over at the time but had undoubtedly scarred them both. In fact, in recent months, their traumatic past had come under great scrutiny, after an unexpected turn of events.

Just a year previously, in 1996, Sandra had read in her local paper, 'The Hull Daily Mail', that Cruse were looking for volunteers to train as bereavement counsellors. Immediately, she'd recalled how helpful they had been to her, following her mother's death and she thought it would be appropriate, if she could help others in the same way. She'd duly applied and it wasn't long before she was invited for training.

She'd progressed well but then had come a proviso.

'Before you can become a fully -fledged counsellor, you will need to have your own period of counselling, just to ensure you have no issues of your own,' a staff member explained.

Sandra had willingly accepted this offer, although she had no idea at the time, of the huge impact of this decision. At her previous bout of counselling, after her mother's death, she had only ever talked about her struggle to cope with her loss. This time, at regular sessions with a female psychotherapist, she'd shared all the many painful issues that had haunted her for so long which came as a huge release. She had also learnt useful coping strategies to help her live with her underlying sadness.

However, there was still the ongoing problem with Danny which counselling alone could not solve. Sandra was determined to maintain contact with her brother and meet up as often as they could. These visits generally went well but there was always a silent barrier – his feelings about his past and his ongoing drinking habit. He generally tutted and turned his head away whenever she mentioned them.

Sadly, Christine had finally had enough and walked out on Danny, taking Alex with her, although she agreed to stay in contact. This latest development pushed Sandra to conclude, she must say something, even if Danny protested.

On his next visit to Hull, as they sat together in Sandra's living room, she spoke her feelings aloud.

'Danny, please will you try to stop drinking. I want us to grow old together.'

Danny immediately took hold of her arm, keen to reassure her.

'Don't worry Sandra, we will grow old together,' he promised.

Despite her doubts, Sandra tried to remain optimistic but she could see how much his health had deteriorated. On his departure, tears were in her eyes as she gave him a goodbye hug. Was there a possibility she would never see him again?

Back in Brighton, the situation became ever more serious. Danny was admitted into Brighton and Sussex University Hospital where he was diagnosed with a fatty liver, indicating long term damage. The doctors warned him that this would lead to cirrhosis, if he didn't stop drinking.

In May, 2008, Sandra received a call from Christine. It wasn't good news. She explained Danny was becoming increasingly ill, losing blood from his back passage and suffering severe stomach pain.

Sandra immediately arranged a visit, catching the seven o'clock train to London, then on to Brighton for half- eleven. On her arrival at Danny's flat, she could see for herself that he was struggling, not just physically but financially as well. He couldn't afford any heating but had the oven on to try and keep warm, though it was ineffective. He offered to transfer his mattress into the living room so Sandra could sleep on it but he couldn't muster the strength to lift it.

Sandra tried to be positive and appear cheerful. She encouraged him to talk of their childhood. They reminisced about their days in Heaton Park, collecting bonfire wood together and sledging down hills on cardboard. Again, they spoke of the delicious cake their mother made in a roasting tin but nothing was said about their father.

But Sandra couldn't leave him without trying again.

'Danny, I'll give you part of my liver, if only you can stop drinking, for three months at least,' she begged, gripping him by the arm.

But immediately Danny brushed her hand aside and insisted, 'The hospital said there's nothing wrong with me.'

Sandra knew differently but she left it at that. What could she could do, except try to be there for him. Perhaps, she decided, it would be a good idea to buy him a mobile phone – at least then he'd be able to call the doctor if needed .. and she could keep in touch with him.

During one particular phone call in June, Danny sounded more upbeat, 'I'm going to spend time with a friend, he has a barge on the canal' he explained, hoping it would reassure his sister. 'I'll take a bottle of rum to set me up and I'll have a great weekend.'

Sandra was pleased to think he wasn't going to be alone but then came words she didn't want to hear.

'And I'm cancelling my hospital appointment in July. My stomach's a lot better since I've been taking some new tablets.'

Now Sandra was furious. She had tried so long to hide her true feelings but this time he had gone too far. 'Don't you dare cancel that appointment!' she remonstrated. But still Danny wouldn't listen. Sandra found herself begging now, her voice quivering with emotion, 'Please Danny, please listen to me. If you carry on like this, you are going to die. Don't you care? What's going to happen to your son Alex?'

But there was no response. Danny had neither the strength nor the will to listen. Over the following days, Sandra sent him money for food but she doubted if it was used for that. His friend wrote him a letter, urging him to stop but it too was ignored. Worst of all, Alex, his fifteen year old son, similarly pleaded with his father to seek help for his addiction but to no avail. He was past help; the drink had destroyed his health and had blurred his mind so much he could not see the reality of what he was doing to himself.

Alex came round to his flat one Wednesday in August and found his father slumped on the living room floor. The drink had finally done its worst and at just fifty-eight years of age, his life had been tragically cut short.

Totally distraught at the shocking scene, Alex immediately called the ambulance but he knew it was too late for his father. Along with the ambulance, the police came and helped organise the removal of his body.

When Sandra heard the shocking news, she travelled down to Brighton to make the funeral arrangements. She needed to visit the flat to collect the necessary papers. After speaking to the coroner, he warned her that the flat was still in a bad way but nothing could have prepared her for the reality of it. The sight that met her was heart-breaking.

The bathroom, bedroom and sitting room were all splattered in blood, with a horrific half -filled bucket of blood by the bed. Poignantly, the bedroom curtains were smeared with two red hand imprints. Sandra was tortured with the thought that he must have been clawing at the window, desperately hoping to attract someone, anyone's attention in his last hours.

The room was freezing, just as it had always been, for Sandra recalled how Danny would never have the money to put in the meter, resulting in him being permanently cold.

Most significantly, there was a visual reminder of the very cause of his demise. The one thing he did spend money on, day after day. For there, next to the mattress on the floor, was an empty wine bottle.

Even more distressing, Sandra's eyes alighted on his old chair, where the tattered remains of an old brown flecked jumper lay. Sandra went over to pick it up. It was so worn-out; it virtually fell apart in her hands yet still recognisable as the very jumper she had knitted him after their first reunion. Grief overwhelmed her, as she hugged it to her body and sobbed uncontrollably.

As she moved around the room, clearing things away, there were further reminders of their past. Hung on the wall was an embroidery, now faded but still instantly recognisable as the one her mother had crafted and which Sandra had given Danny several years earlier. In a drawer, she found some beautiful Polish wafers, etched with religious pictures, and still in their wrapper. Sandra was pleased to see them, encouraged to think that her brother had purchased them as a reminder of his family's traditional Polish Easter and Christmas celebrations. She placed them in her pocket, with the intention of keeping them, as a lasting reminder of Danny.

Her pain was intense and although her continued counselling was a great help, she still felt bereft. She had worked so hard and searched for so many years to make contact with her brother, only to lose him in such tragic circumstances. She tortured herself with regrets but felt ultimately he was very much a victim of circumstance. If only Kazik had not had such high expectation of his son, then maybe he wouldn't have rebelled. If only Kazik hadn't abandoned the family, just when Danny needed a father so much, then maybe he wouldn't have felt so angry. If only Danny hadn't disappeared when Sandra married, believing that nobody needed him, when in truth they missed him dreadfully. If only Danny hadn't been too embarrassed to admit his drink problem to his family and sought them out for help, maybe he would still be around. Now it was too late, for all the 'if onlys' would never bring him back.

But nor was it fair to put the blame on Kazik for Danny's demise. He had his 'if onlys' too. If only he hadn't lost his parents when he was ten, if only he hadn't been forcibly transported by the Russians into the gulag, his mental illness might not have developed and probably he wouldn't have suffered his acute paranoia. The 'if onlys' continued over the weeks to come.

Danny's funeral was a simple affair attended by only a few friends. It was a humanist service and afterwards his ashes were scattered in the local river where he had enjoyed spending time on his friend's barge. Sad that she had no grave to visit, Sandra decided to have a tree planted in a cemetery in Brighton, with a simple plaque of remembrance.

As well as her own grief, Sandra felt immense sadness and sympathy for fifteen year old Alex – he was too young to cope with everything he'd witnessed during his formative years. She was particularly concerned as to the effect his father's demise might have on him in the future.

As she tried to cope with her anguish, her immediate family were a great support and they became ever more precious, as the frailty of life had become such a stark reality.

It led her to consider Kazik's one remaining brother Janek, who was now in his eighties and his sister Werca who was even older. She must try to see them again whilst they were still alive so with that intention, she contacted Weisiek, Janek's son, to arrange a visit.

It was several weeks later that John drove her over to Poland to stay with the family in Wasilkow. It was another very emotional reunion.

'Why don't you make this your home? I will build you a house and you and John can live here permanently,' her uncle suggested.

Sandra appreciated this offer but whilst she'd always cherished her Polish roots, she did not wish to leave Britain. But his kindness meant such a lot to her. How happy Kazik would have been to know how much she enjoyed sharing time with his extended family. It was Kazik who had made her learn Polish from the moment of her birth and although not grateful at the time, she now valued being able to communicate with her Polish cousins and chat about better times.

But, perhaps most significantly, she valued the fact that she could go to Poland whenever she wanted, for it was no longer under communist rule and its people were free to live and worship in their own way.

Over the following years, these visits became increasingly important to Sandra as she felt it was an ideal way, indeed the only way, in which she could reconnect with the Polish side of her family that she had lost when her parents and brother died.

However, there was still one area that was not accessible – the area known as White Russia, formerly eastern Poland, which sadly included Zupran. It was still under Soviet control and came with extensive restrictions. Sandra was disappointed that she had never been able to visit her father's childhood home.

Then in 2017, the situation changed. A visa was no longer required if your stay was to be less than five days, which meant a visit was much more viable. Sandra discussed this situation with her cousin Wiesiek and together they made plans to go to Zupran, along with John, to see for the first time where their respective fathers had spent their childhoods.

As they entered the village with its wooden huts, simple mud roads and its meandering river, they imagined that life hadn't changed too much over the past eighty years. When they met up with one of their cousins Danusia who still lived there, she confirmed their assumptions were correct. Living conditions were very basic with extremely primitive sanitation and no running water in the houses. Yet everyone was friendly and uncomplaining, showing a degree of toughness that Sandra admired.

Despite this hardship, Sandra could appreciate the reasons for her father's love of his homeland. Those magnificent pine forests, where he and his brothers had picked mushrooms and collected firewood, still retained their grandeur but were now completely safe to wander through and enjoy.

Even more wonderful, after the family's years of immense hardship, it was also good to acknowledge that several hectares of this forest area still belonged to the Szwabowicz family and that was truly a source of genuine pride.

Sandra was pleased to have an opportunity to visit the graves of her much respected paternal grandparents, Antonio and Wladystawa. She was delighted that Wiesiek had arranged for memorial plaques to be placed on their plot, as a permanent tribute to them. She found the whole visit profoundly emotional and memorable.

She had always recognised her father's constant wish – his ultimate dream - for his family to retain their Polish culture and identity and she returned home, forever determined to do just that.

Today, in 2018, she adheres to certain Polish customs and regularly cooks Polish food, especially at Christmas time. She has brought up Colette, her daughter and Sophia, her granddaughter to also consider Poland as their second home.

The bison Kazik gave his daughter as a parting gift, still proudly sits on Sandra's mantle-piece at home and the Polish wafers she found in Danny's possession, lay in her drawer. A compelling photo of her grandfather, Antonio, graces her hall, as he looks out on her, resplendent in his smart military uniform.

They are all constant reminders of her family's hidden past but now Sandra can look to a brighter future - for the Szwabowicz family truly lives on. None of Kazik's siblings are alive today, with the death of Kazik's last sister in 2016, but they have many descendants who are eager to keep in touch. Sandra and her family visit them whenever they can.

Sadly, Sandra still holds one deep regret and heartache – she has been unable to trace any members of the family from her mother's side- the Poleszczuks. She is still desperate to find out what happened to her maternal grandfather, Francis Poleszczuk, the doctor whose fate is unknown. Despite extensive research, every enquiry has so far drawn a blank. The International Tracing Service has explained that many Warsaw records were destroyed during the war. It seems probable that he and the remainder of his family were completely wiped out by the German atrocities but it would be comforting for Sandra to discover the truth. She is justifiably proud of them, especially her mother's resilience and fortitude, despite the immense horrors she underwent.

Slowly, on completion of her counselling and after shedding countless healing tears, Sandra has finally been able to confront her parent's suffering and put most dark thoughts behind her. At last, she feels free from the secrets that bound her and with that freedom has come a realisation that she must no longer remain silent about everything her parents underwent, even though they, themselves, never referred to it. She wants the world to hear of the scale of this human tragedy and to bring alive all those many unspoken words.

EPILOGUE

Many of the thousands of Polish prisoners of war, who arrived in Britain in the early 1940s, never spoke about their incarceration; often because they were so traumatised, they blanked it out. Others felt if they publically complained it would jeopardise their loved ones who were still trapped behind the Iron Curtain. As for Kazik, he was officially instructed to put his experiences behind him and never speak to anyone of what he'd experienced. Maria was similarly advised to forget her ordeal. Was this sound advice or did it have a negative impact on their recovery? If they had had the opportunity to explore their innermost feelings and express their darkest thoughts, might their future lives have been less blighted by the evil that was bestowed on them?

Certainly, on their arrival in Britain, as displaced persons, it was almost impossible for them to continue living as if these awful times had never happened. Not only was the past unforgettable, their hidden trauma overshadowed their thinking, their attitudes and their behaviour on a daily basis. For Kazik and his long suffering family, his inner torment was conveyed in every blank stare, in every angry word and in every dark mood which sadly sometimes led to unprovoked violence. In the end, his dreadful experiences not only destroyed his marital relationship but impacted on his family life to such an extent, it damaged the next generation too.

Initially, the couple's mutual understanding and appreciation of each other's brutal experiences, at the hands of Stalin and Hitler, drew them together. Maria, particularly, showed a determination to hold on to her marriage, however difficult it was at times, for she had lost so much in the past. She rarely complained of her lot but simply endured her many trials without self –pity, in an attempt to face the future positively. But both of them were deeply scarred – for Kazik this was most evident in his mental illness whereas Maria suffered constantly with physical health problems.

For Sandra, the daughter of Kazik and Maria, recounting this poignant story has taken her on a very difficult but worthwhile journey. For Sandra was held in the grip of her parent's past. Her childhood was overshadowed by her father's disturbing behaviour and her mother's puzzling silent acceptance of it.

Now, by discovering their secrets, she is no longer bound by them and instead wants the world to know that when her parents' actions seemed strange, even unacceptable at times, it was purely a result of the dreadful effects of their incarceration. Sandra is adamant that her father had the capacity to be a loving and compassionate father and that his irrational and rather aggressive behaviour was attributable to his mental illness, which in turn was exacerbated by his awful war time experiences. She recognises that her mother was a victim of an appalling tragedy which resulted in her many physical problems whilst also giving her a steely edge and a great stoicism to passively accept whatever life threw at her.

Out of this story, comes   great courage and great hope. Ultimately whilst evil has done its worst, it has not won. Kazik throughout his entire ordeal was determined to keep his Polish roots and to that end, he brought up his children to speak Polish and to visit and enjoy Poland from a young age. Undoubtedly, he would have been equally delighted to know his ultimate goal has been fulfilled - his sacrifice was not in vain. The country he loved so much is now free of communism and Sandra can go and enjoy travelling there, largely without restriction.

Surely there are lessons here to be learnt by everyone. Amidst all this unimaginable suffering, we can see and understand that evil does not have to have the final say. It is good to be reminded that the human mind and spirit are able to exist and survive even when all hope appears to be lost.

This story is also immensely powerful in showing us both the depths of human depravity but equally the resilience and fortitude of mankind and the overwhelming impact of love, especially within a close family.

Finally, in the telling of this story, we have all gained a greater insight into the vital and outstanding contribution of the Poles during the Second World War. The Polish Second Corps were instrumental in the defeat of the Germans in North Africa and Italy. Many of them, including Kazik, were heroes and the British owe them a huge debt of gratitude.

Sandra too has shown great resolve. She has found the courage to talk about her parent's past quite openly; she has broken through their enforced silence, revealing a story which the world definitely needs to hear.

APPENDAGE

Sophia, John and Sandra's grand-daughter, was deeply affected when told of the lives of her ancestors and the horrors the Poles endured under the Nazis and Soviets. As an eleven year old, in her first year at South Holderness Senior School, she wrote this heart felt poem which expresses her feelings about the war.

People dead all over the floor
No one there anymore
People who are alive are too scared to even cry
No sound of planes
But they're still scared as they try not to cry
Wondering if their mum or dad are still alive
Hoping it will be over soon
Sat lonely in the street where their house used to be.

ACKNOWLEDGMENTS

I would like to thank the following people for their valuable contribution to this book:

Sandra Spooner, my kind neighbour, for trusting me to write her deeply personal family story and for contributions from her husband John. It took many, many hours and often reignited painful - as well as some happy - memories for her, as together we researched and uncovered her parent's past.

Irena Czernichowska at The Hoover Institution, Stanford, USA

Louise Williams - Lothian Health Services Archivist

Margaret Goddard -APC Polish Enquiries, Ministry of Defence

J Kowalska , Polish Institute & Sikorski Museum , London

Andy Gill, the printer, for his professional advice and valuable help with the cover design and layout of the book.

And finally......

Clive, my husband, for his unlimited patience and support during our research and the extensive time he spent in helpful discussion and editing of the final script. His contribution has been immense.

BIBLIOGRAPHY

The Polish Community in Manchester & the North West -
T W Scragg

Poland's Contribution to the Allied victory in the Second World
War – A Suchcitz

'Gulag' - A Applebaum

Two years in a Gulag – F Pleszak

Forgotten Voices of the Holocaust – L Smith

Stalin's Ethnic Cleansing in Eastern Poland- Tales of the Deported
1940-46

The Eagle Unbowed- Poland and the Poles in WW2 -
H Kochanski

A History of Nazi Concentration Camps – N Wachsmann

Stalin –Waiting for Hitler 1929- 1941 – S Kotkin

A Memoir of the Warsaw Uprising – M Bialoszewski